D0509868

MASTERFUL MINDBENDERS

MASTERFUL MINDBENDERS

TREVOR TRURAN

First published in 1984 by
Octopus Books Limited
59 Grosvenor Street
London W1

© 1984 Hennerwood Publications Limited

ISBN 0 86273 126 7

Printed and bound in Great Britain by
Collins Glasgow

Illustrations by Andrew Martin,
Brian Mayor,
Neil Sayer

CONTENTS

INTRODUCTION

The aim in offering these puzzles is to amuse and entertain and not to baffle with specialist knowledge, complex chains of thought or devious tricks. There are ten chapters which will keep you happily occupied in various ways without, it is hoped, too much mental strain. The puzzles are graded ? to ??? to give you a rough idea of the level of difficulty (? being the easiest and ??? the toughest) so that you can make a selection according to age or inclination.

Now, off you go and enjoy a mind-bending experience!

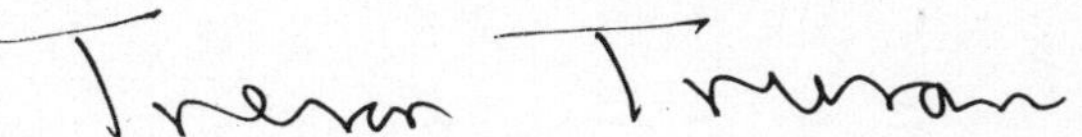

ODD MAN OUT

Can you spot the one black sheep in each family? In most cases, the trick is to work out what joins the rest together. Only simple general knowledge and powers of observation are required here.

In any group there is always one 'odd man out' – at parties it is usually me. Who else can enter a roomful of evening dress and glittering jewellery without taking his bicycle clips off; kiss the back of his hostess's hand – the one holding the glass of champagne – and tell the vicar that if he'd known it was fancy dress he would have turned up as Henry VIII?

The trouble with any gathering is that it is always possible, in a negative way, to make any one member the odd one out. A quick flash of the optics over

HAT COAT GLOVE SHOE UMBRELLA SCARF

and you could say that SHOE is the odd one out as none of the others are, usually, worn on the feet. Ditto any of the others for a variety of reasons.

What is missing here is, if SHOE does not belong, what *positive* link is there which connects all the others but which still excludes SHOE?

In looking at the list it is better, perhaps, to look for the link which joins all but one of the members together – in this case HAT, GLOVE, COAT, SHOE, SCARF are all *worn* – an UMBRELLA isn't.

In the puzzles which follow, award yourself 3 points for every answer you give which agrees with our solution and, as a special sale offer, 1 point for any other answer you come up with, which you can convince a *sensible* friend is correct!

1(?)

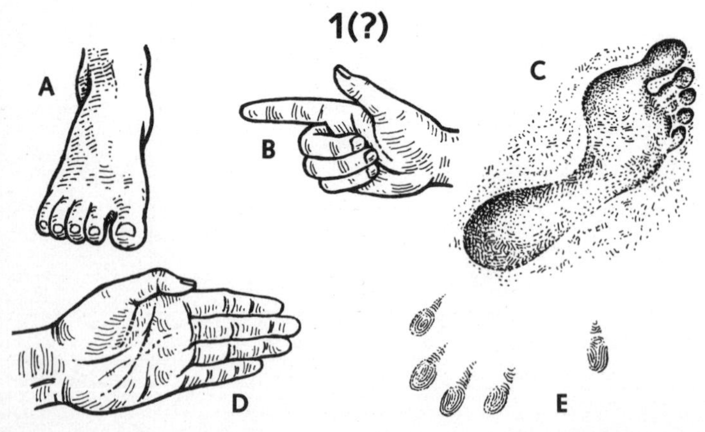

SOLUTION ON PAGE 169.

2(?)

THIRTYSIX NINE EIGHTYONE FOUR FIFTYFOUR ONE TWENTYFIVE

3(?)

4(?)

BROWN PINK RED YELLOW GREEN BLACK WHITE BLUE ORANGE

5(?)

MARS JUPITER URANUS VENUS SATURN NEPTUNE

SOLUTIONS ON PAGES 169 AND 170.

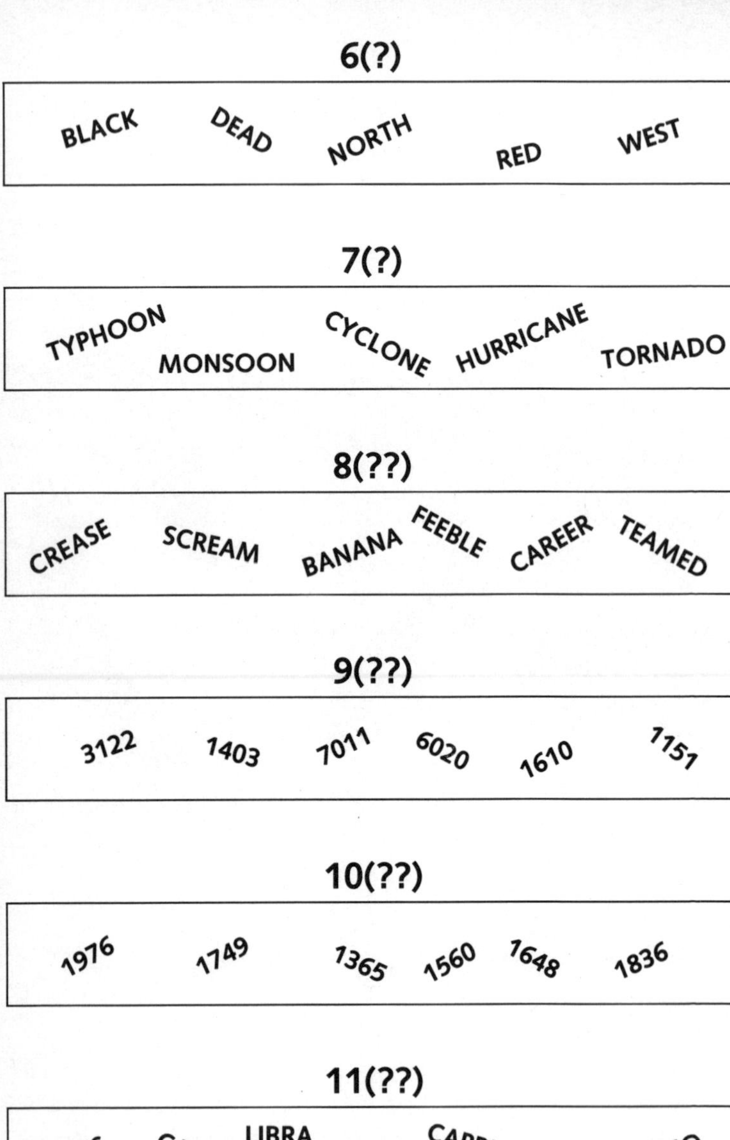

SOLUTIONS ON PAGES 169 AND 170.

12(??)

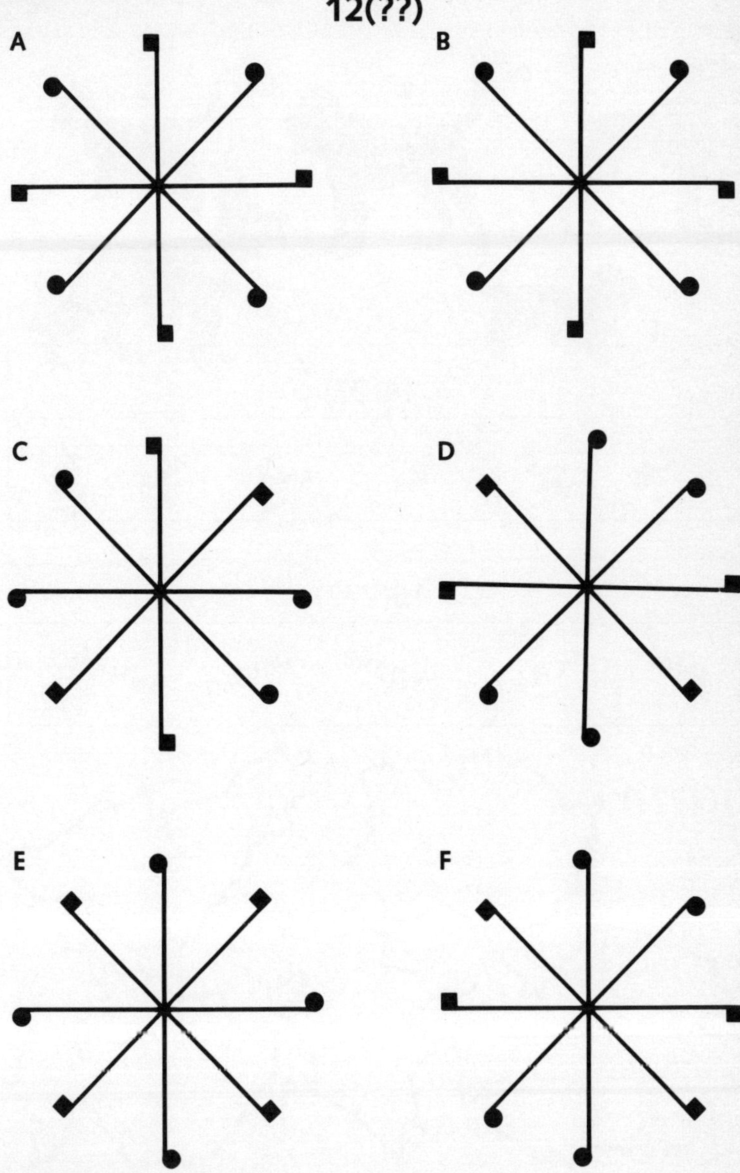

SOLUTION ON PAGE 170.

13(??)

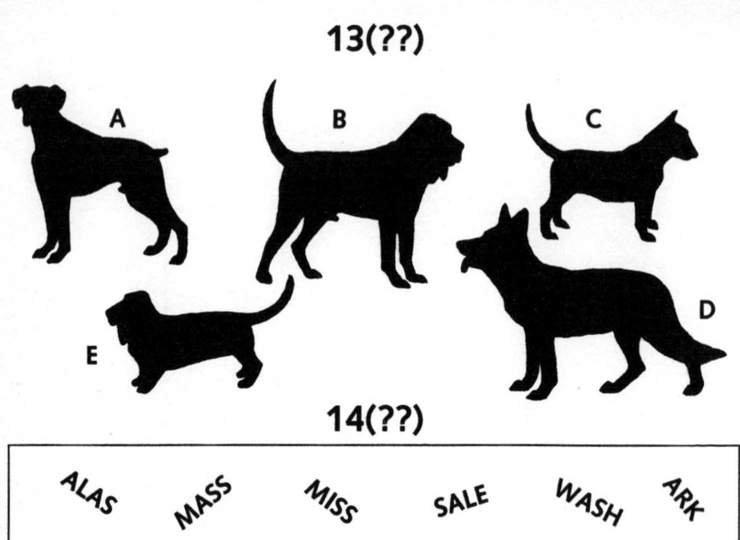

14(??)

ALAS MASS MISS SALE WASH ARK

15(???)

JAMES MICHAEL EDWARD HAROLD ALEC ANTHONY

16(???)

SOLUTIONS ON PAGES 169 AND 170.

17(???)

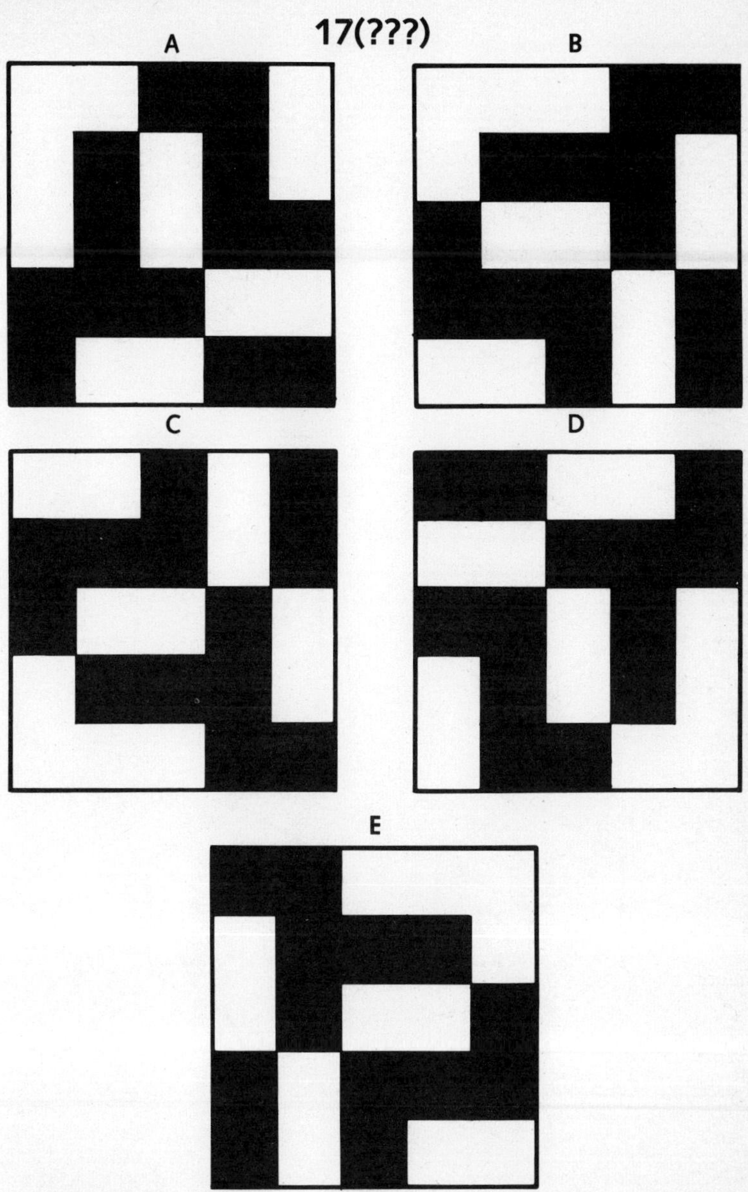

SOLUTION ON PAGE 170.

18(???)

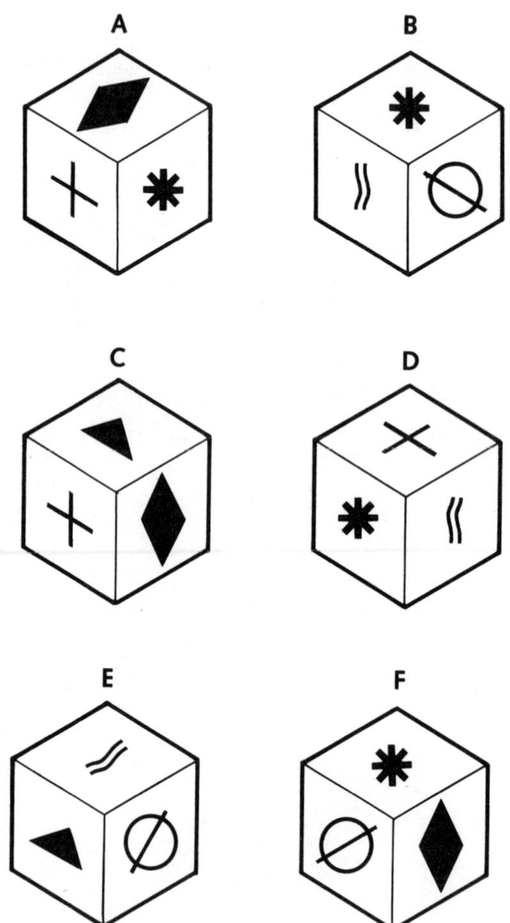

SOLUTION ON PAGE 170.

19(???)

SOLUTION ON PAGE 170.

20(???)

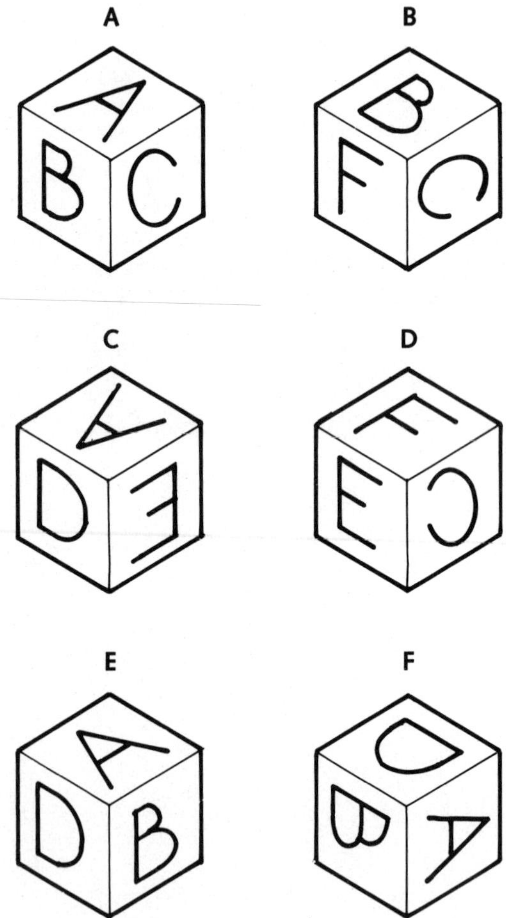

SOLUTION ON PAGE 169.

BITS AND PIECES

Can your eyes feed your brain with the right information to tell your hand how to be a cut above the rest? Strawberry Shares lets you practise in safety the party-giver's perennial problem – how to cut a decorated cake to give a fair share of the iced delights to each eater. There are also pictorial puzzles for you to ponder over.

Half-Caked Idea (?)

Mrs Little had a problem. Whenever she had a cake to share between her two children, the arguments as to who should have which piece made the neighbours think World War Three had started early.

However carefully she made the cut, when she served up the pieces both children would protest that their 'half' was smaller.

One day she had an idea. She called the children into the kitchen, stood them beside the table where the cake and the cake knife lay and said something which at once put an end to all argument.
What did she tell the children to do, so that neither could complain about the share of cake each received?

Strawberry Shares (? & ??)

The neat solution to the last puzzle becomes impossible when the cake has to be cut into several pieces and the cake has been brightly decorated. Everybody has to have an equal share of the cake and many a gimlet eye will be fixed on the server to make sure they do not miss out on a star, a strawberry or a blob of cream.

To increase your skill in this difficult art we have asked a master chef to prepare a dozen decorated delights, enough for a jubilee street party.

He has carefully added lines made from hundreds and thousands along which the cake can be cut.

In each case, every person must have an equal sized share – though they do not have to have the same shape as each other. And each must have the same number of each decoration as everybody else.
Can you draw in the lines to show how the cake should be divided up?
(Hint – if each person has, say, just one star then where two stars are next to each other there must be a cut along the line between them – fill these lines in first and the rest will be, dare we say it, a piece of cake!)

SOLUTION ON PAGE 169.

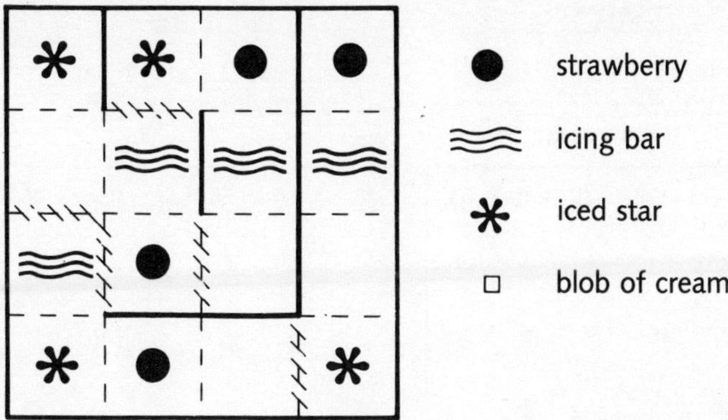

4 pieces 1 iced star, 1 icing bar, 1 strawberry in each piece. There must be a cut wherever the same symbols are in adjacent squares. There can only be one empty square in each piece as well so there must be a cut where empty squares are next door. The hatch line shows how the cutting must be completed.

ONE

6 pieces 1 iced star, 1 icing bar, 1 strawberry in each.

SOLUTION ON PAGE 171.

TWO

6 pieces 1 star, 1 bar, 1 strawberry in each.

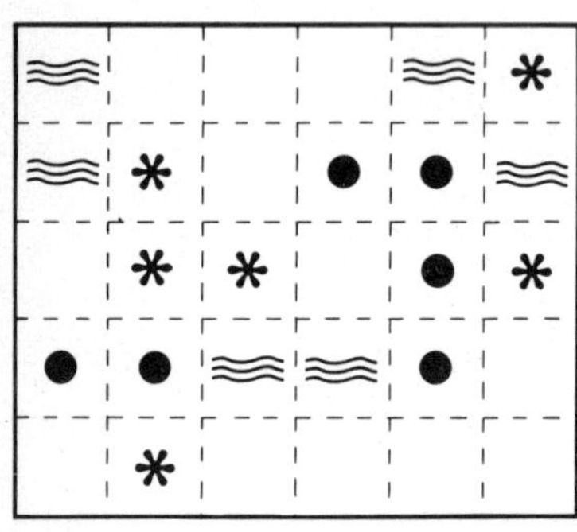

THREE

6 pieces 2 stars, 1 bar, 1 strawberry in each.

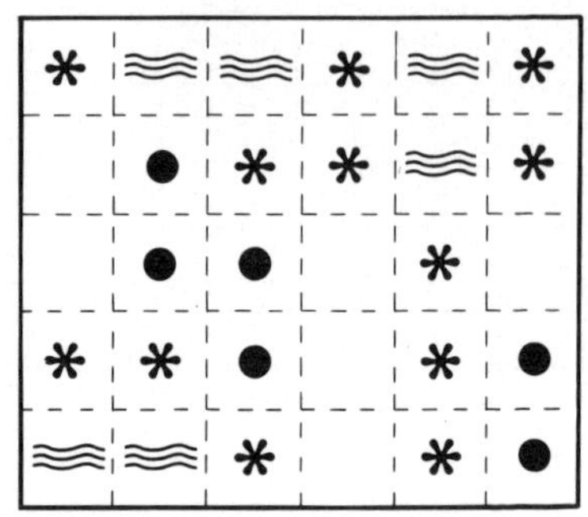

FOUR

6 pieces 1 star, 1 bar in each.

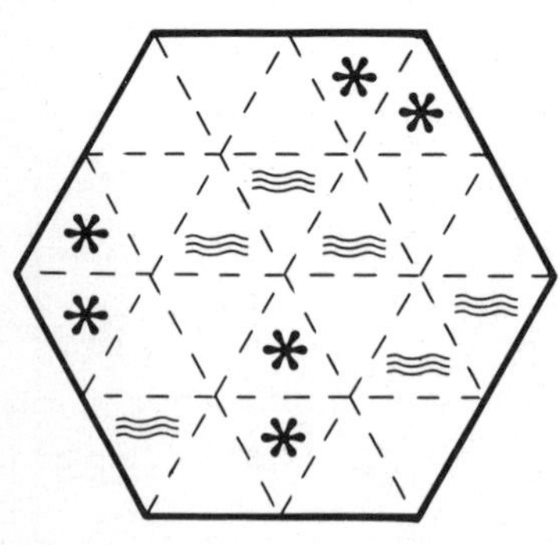

FIVE

6 pieces 1 star, 1 bar, 1 strawberry in each.

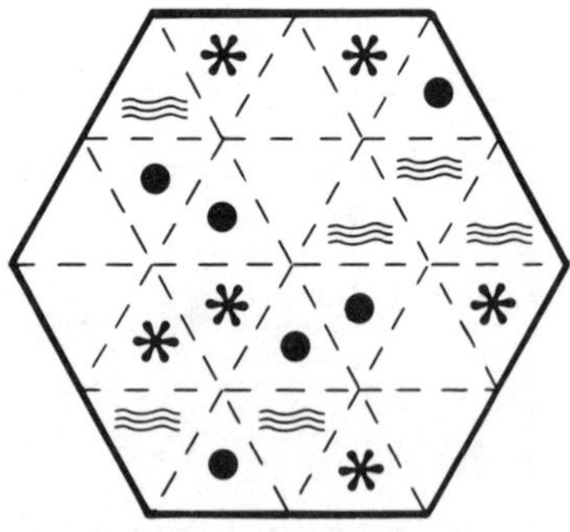

SOLUTIONS ON PAGES 171, 172 and 173.

SIX

3 pieces 3 stars, 1 bar, 3 strawberries in each.

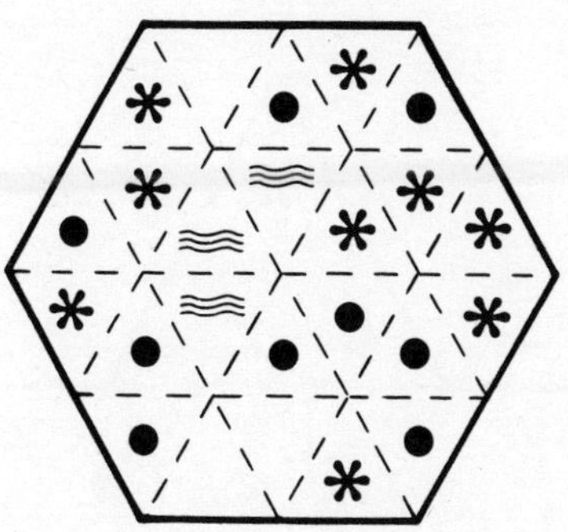

SEVEN

9 pieces 1 star, 1 bar, 1 strawberry, 2 blobs of cream in each.

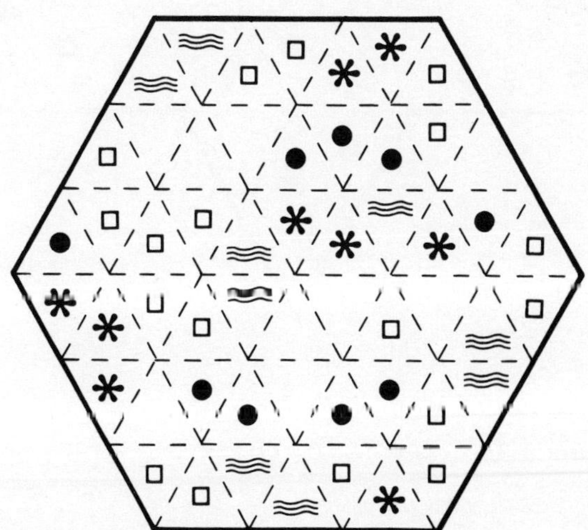

SOLUTIONS ON PAGES 171 AND 172.

EIGHT

12 pieces 1 star, 1 bar, 1 strawberry in each.

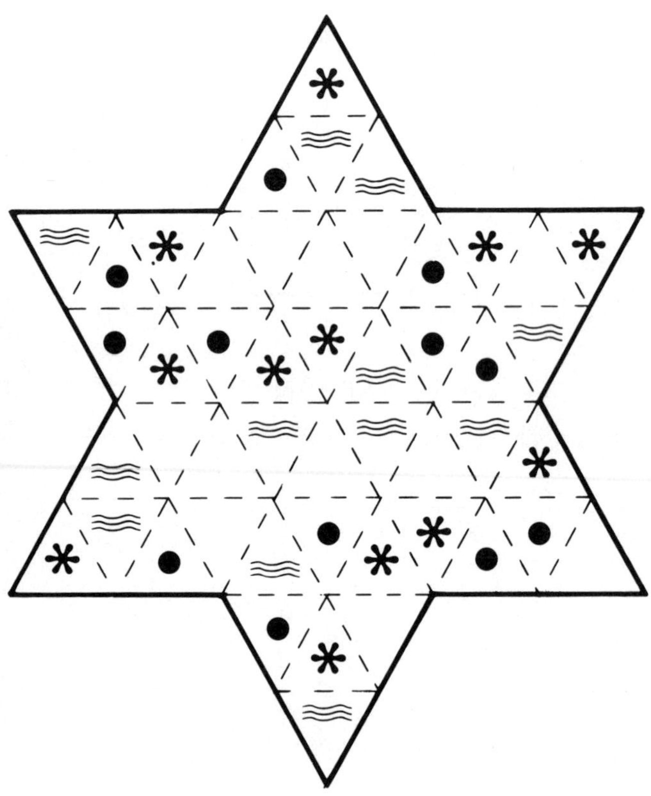

SOLUTION ON PAGE 173.

NINE

5 pieces 1 star, 1 bar, 2 strawberries, 1 blob of cream in each.

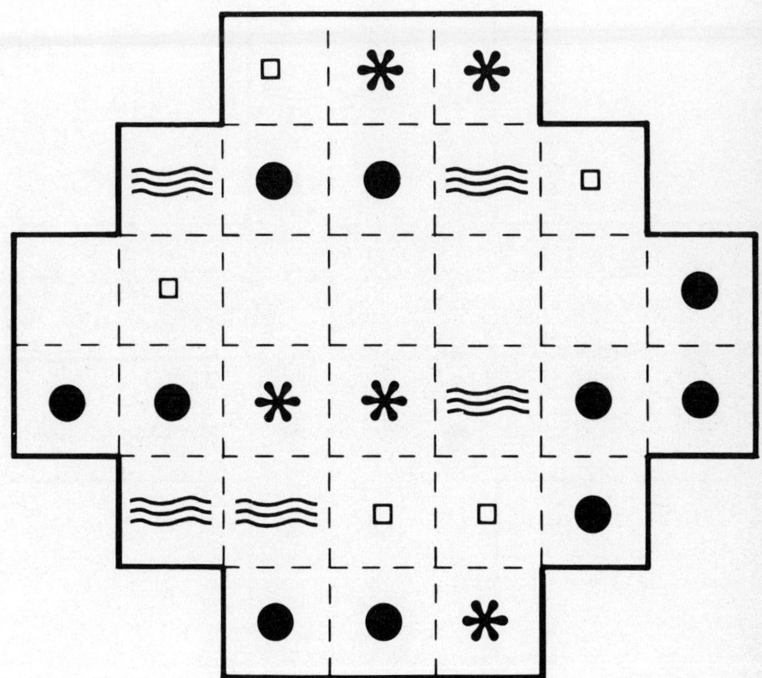

SOLUTION ON PAGE 172.

TEN

9 pieces 1 star, 1 bar, 1 strawberry, 1 blob of cream in each.

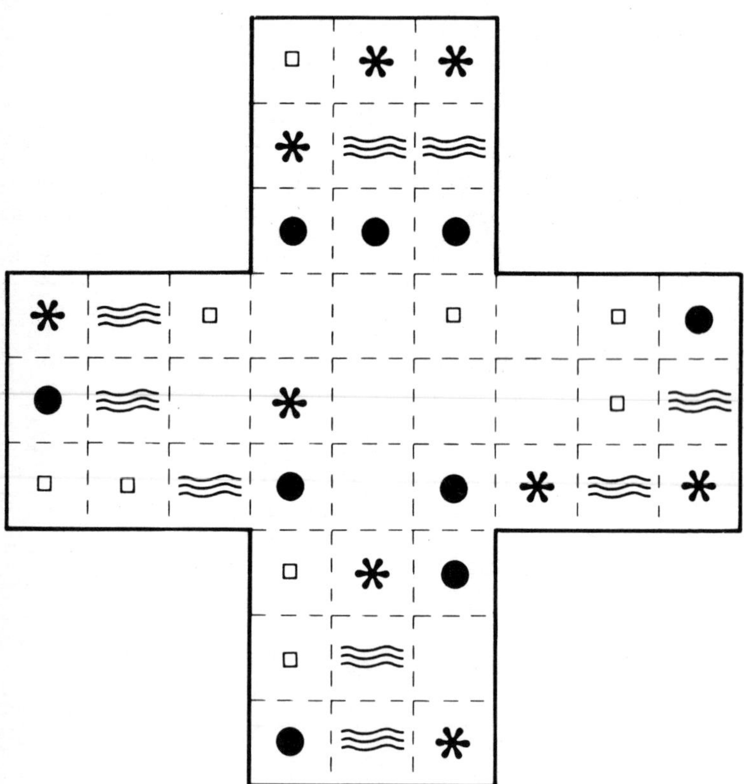

SOLUTION ON PAGE 171.

ELEVEN

12 pieces 1 star, 1 bar, 2 strawberries in each.

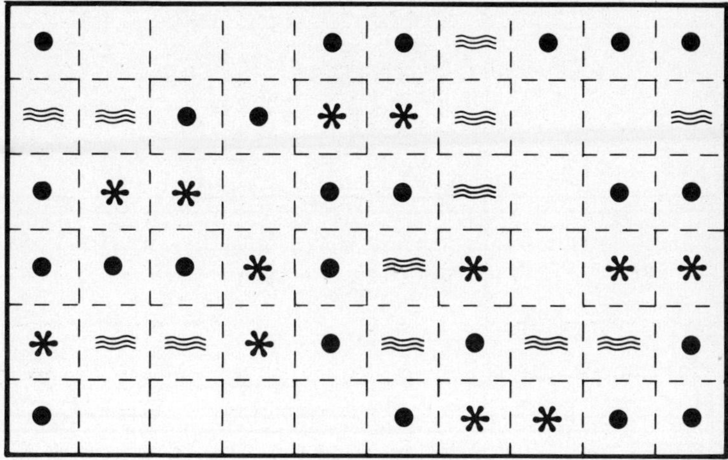

TWELVE

8 pieces 1 star, 2 bars, 2 strawberries, 1 blob of cream in each.

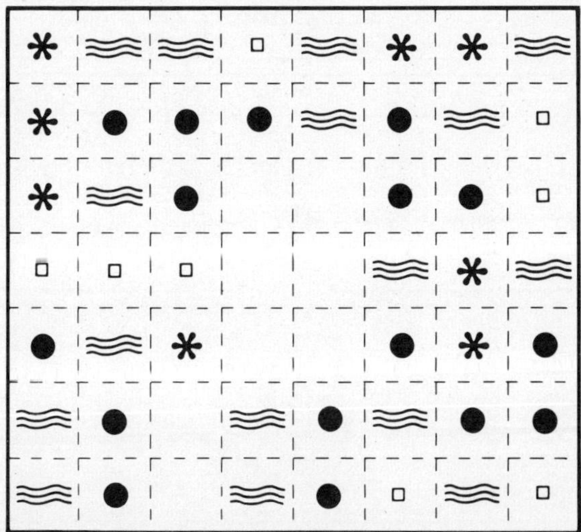

SOLUTIONS ON PAGES 171 AND 172.

In Sequence (?)

Can you put these five pictures into the correct order?

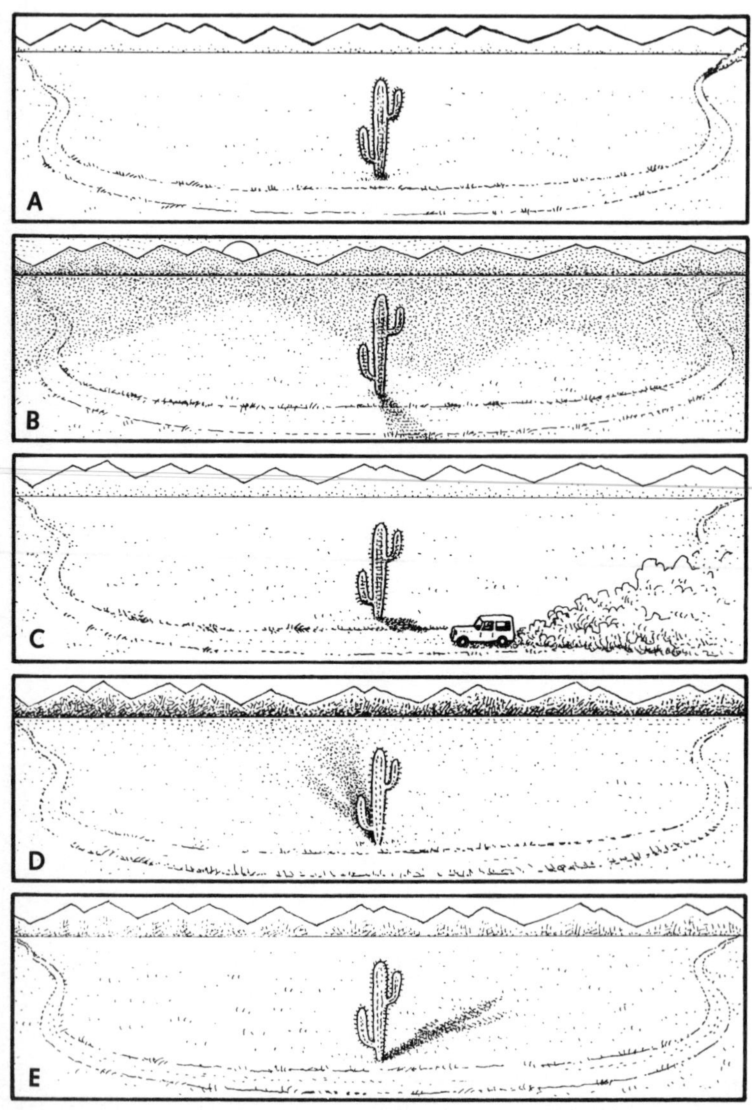

SOLUTION ON PAGE 174.

Party Pieces (?)

These five snaps of Lady Amelia's garden party last summer have been muddled up. Can you work out the order in which they were taken?

SOLUTION ON PAGE 174.

Spot The Difference (?)

When young Justus Thumb tried to break the local arcade's Space Invaders machine record the local press photographer took a picture.

Back at the office another artist tried to improve the quality but made 20 mistakes.

How many of them can you spot?

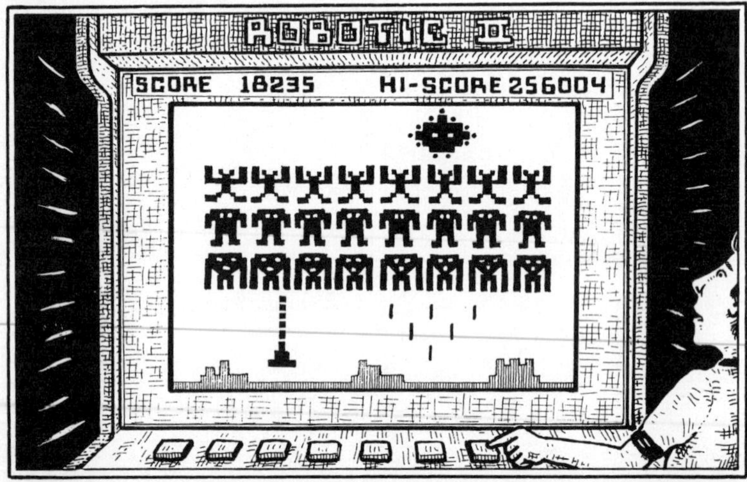

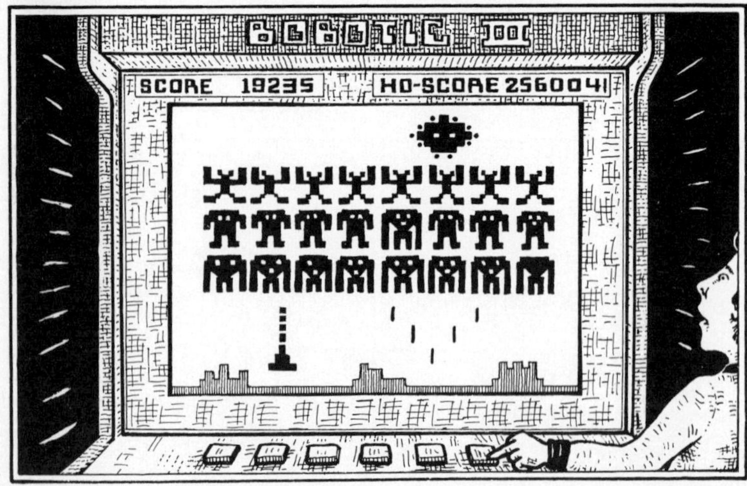

SOLUTION ON PAGE 173.

Cube Bits (??)

A 2 × 2 × 2 cube is to be made from eight unit cubes. Each face of the big cube will be entirely in one of the six colours. The faces of the unit cubes which touch inside the big cube will be black.
Can the big cube be made with these eight small cubes?

Any face on a small cube which you cannot see is black.

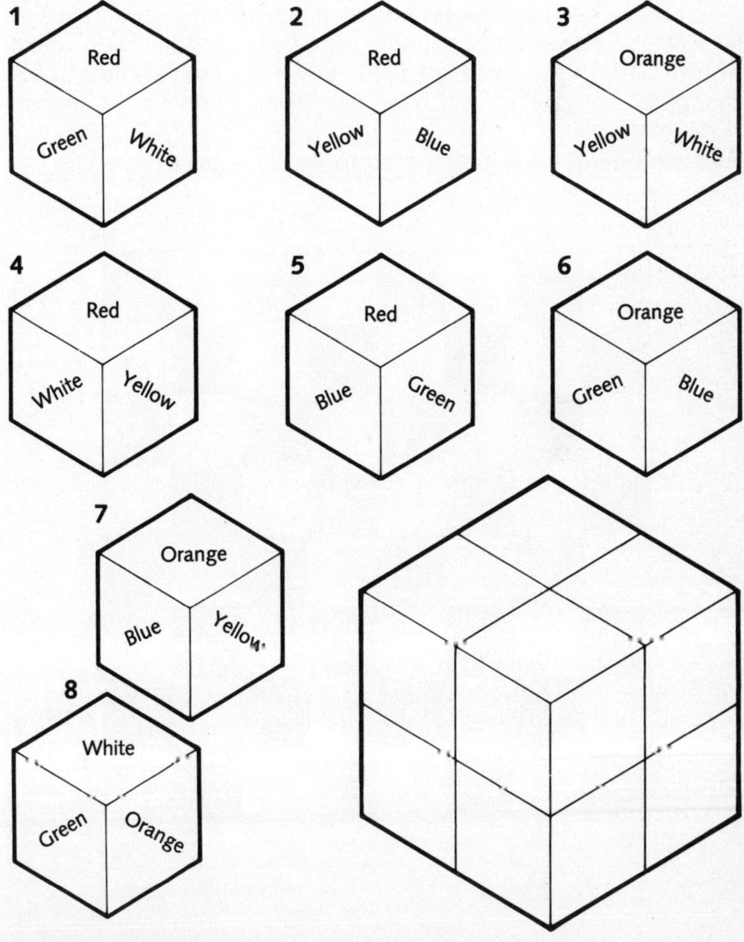

SOLUTION ON PAGE 174.

The Winning Cut (??)

While Mrs Little is busy making more cakes, Mr Little is learning a bitter lesson – that children play to their own rules and that buying cheap can be a mistake.

Like the draughts board and pieces made from felt and cut from the packet with a modelling knife.

It was cheap, quick and easy – just as the advert had promised. But it also made it possible, just when he was assured of victory, for young Cheryl to literally turn the tables at a stroke.

Her one Queen against his four men looked hopeless and just as he was about to suggest that she resign with honour there was a sudden flash of the modelling knife, a blur of hands and felt and a change in the situation which left her taking all four of his men in one move!

Just what did the naughty girl do to win that game?

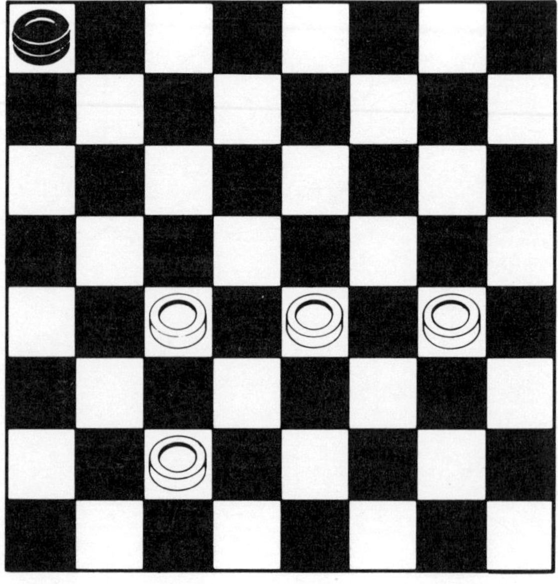

BLACK: Cheryl **WHITE: Dad**

SOLUTION ON PAGE 174.

RIDDLES

Strike up the band, lift the curtain, sit back and indulge in a host of entertaining jokes, stories, verses and strange situations. You are also invited to take part in the famous head-to-head confrontation, What's My Blank?

What's My Blank (? & ??)

In this little word puzzle, derived from a certain TV programme which you may have seen, you will be given a series of clues, like blank something or something blank. You are then invited to make your choice of one of the several possibilities which may occur to you.

If you make the right choice of answers, then the initial letters will spell out yet another word – and that is the solution you are seeking.

To make the thing a bit easier you have a couple of clues:

1 The length of the missing word is given or here and there the middle letters may already be in place.
2 A cryptic clue is offered to the solution word.

In case you are still feeling a bit blank yourself, cast a spare eye or two over this example.

Note: the number of blanks in this type of puzzle equals the number of letters.

----- bank	B	lood
----- ---- cabin	U	ncle Tom's
----- rose	T	udor
--- leaf	T	ea
---- due	O	ver
Bird's ----	N	est

Clue: Connected with clothing.
So the answer is button.

Sometimes the answer will be not one but two words, one given by the initial letters and the other by the last letters of the answers. These two words will always have a strong association, as do CAT NAP, the solution to the example at the top of the next page.

Note: the number of blanks in this type of puzzle does not equal the number of letters.

Tin -----	C	a	N
----- bet!	A	lph	A
----- door	T	ra	P

Clue: What a domestic pet may have.

ONE (?)

---- handed		
Treasure ------		
Special -----		
Royal ----		

Clue: An animal.

TWO (?)

Solar -----		
Soft ------		
------ apple		
Marble ----		
--- nail		
Blood ------		

Clue: A vegetable.

SOLUTIONS ON PAGE 174.

THREE (?)

------ ticket		
---- duckling		
--- meter		
----- sauce		
--- doll		

Clue: Bought at the grocer's.

FOUR (?)

----- top		LIF	
----- shower		PRI	
Dr -----			
Evening -----		RES	
Light -----		EAR	

Clue: Part of the fun of the fair.

FIVE (?)

First -----		LAS	
----- street		IG	
Look -----		NT	
Bicycle -----		UM	

Clue: Where you find newspapers and grease.

SOLUTIONS ON PAGE 174.

SIX (?)

Sweet -----		
Hammer and -----		
Arabian ------		
---- washer		
------ whale		
----- time		
---- up		
----- line		
Water ----		
---- worm		
------ parade		
Green -------		

Clue: You carry it around in your pocket.

SEVEN (?)

---- glass		IN	
----- tube		NNE	
----- rash		CTTL	
----- piece		Y	

Clue: Grows in the countryside.

SOLUTIONS ON PAGE 174.

EIGHT (??)

New ----		
Jet ------		
Wedding ----		
Space --------		
---- book		
---- post		
Down -----		
--- ache		

Clue: Something sweet to eat.

A Fir Question (?)

Which film hero wrote this in his newspaper?

My start rhymes with blue,
My middle with fir.
My end rhymes with can
A clue? – south coast county.
Tell me, who must I be?

Gardeners' Question Time (?)

My one, two, three takes you far and wide.
My two, three, four, say, in short, you've arrived.
My four, five, six means to decompose
My whole is a food the gardener grows.

What am I?

SOLUTIONS ON PAGES 174 AND 175.

One, Two, Three ... (?)

My one is in ONE but not in TWO.
My two is in TWO but not in THREE.
My three is in THREE but not in FOUR.
My whole can be seen on hill and moor.

What am I?

Calling All Puzzlers (?)

Some of the letters in each line of our coded message, taken in the order they appear, spell a word whose length is given by the number in brackets at the end. Thus AXTGYESMT (4) would give the word TEST.

If you can find the word in each line a phrase useful to all readers of this book will appear.

KALDEFT (3)
YMOPNGURT (4)
VAPBORZTAINFZ (5)
ETAJSSKFNE (4)
PLQMOZTLXHKE (3)
SMPEEFGTROOAOTINLLY (5)

Crashword (?)

The clues are entered one letter to each square but, as you can see from the letters, they overlap a bit – rather like a line of cars which didn't stop as quickly as the first one. The result is a household object – can you find out what it is?

(a) Is in the past.
(b) Below the knee.
(c) Letter of force.
(d) Short raincoat.
(e) Facial feature.
(f) Isle Of Wight feature.

		b	b	b	b	
a	a	a				c

		f	f	f	f	f
		e	e	e	e	
d	d	d				

SOLUTIONS ON PAGES 175 AND 176.

Jungle Jester (?)

My first is in March but not in hare.
My second in lion but not in lair.
My third in money can be found.
My fourth in sky-high but not in sound.
My fifth and sixth in every and year.
My whole fills the jungle with noise and cheer.

What am I?

Headless Rhyme (?)

here as a oung an rom ee
ho ent or a wim n he ea.
A hark aw is lippers
nd aid 'hoopee ippers!'
hen te he oung an or is ea.

This should have been, Jones the Word thought, a winner at the Sillybillyogogogog Eisteddfod. If only Dai the Print hadn't missed off the first letter of every word which had 2 or more letters in it.

It hadn't been much of a help, though a kind thought, when Dai printed all the missing letters at the bottom of the page; the judges were too far gone to sort it out.
Can you put the letters where they belong and make sense of Jones' masterpiece?

A, A, D, F, F, F, F, H, H, I, K, M, M, S, S, S, S, S, T, T, T, T, T, W, W, W, W, Y, Y.

The Story So Far... (?)

The school magazine was not coming along too well. It had seemed a good idea to form 3K to start one, especially the idea of writing adventure stories in which they were the main characters.

The problem was in the production side; it is difficult for the typesetter to get the text right when the features editor uses the rubber printing outfit as ammunition against the sports editor.

SOLUTIONS ON PAGE 176.

Quite near to tears, the editor stared at the mangled text:

T. . . . y S . . . t and her fri . . . ., Chris . . . her and S . . . ra Ed . . . ds, ... fully t . . . ed the key to the w . . . house door. S . . . ly it began to open, g . . . . ing and g . . . ling like a bear d . . tur . . d dur . . g it w . . ter s . . . p.

Inside the d . . . ness c . . . ded around our s . . . ed heroes; s . . . . ering noises . . . their teeth c . . . . . . ing in f . . . . .. So . . where in this v . . t buil . . . g the c . . . . s had st . . . ed the g . . . bul . . . ..

As they g . . . . d t . . ir way along a m . . ty, s . . lly w . . ., a s . . . ch c . . . . ed on and a br . . . iant sh . . . of light p . . . ed on them.

They were t . . . ped!

With a long sigh the editor, true to her noble calling, crawled around the classroom floor until she had picked up all the missing pieces. She arranged them neatly on her table and began to wonder where each fitted.

aft all and are ark as ash be camp car care cot din ends
hatter he ill in in is lay lee lick lion low me me old race rap
right roan rook rope row row set top urn us war wit

Can you lend a hand and put the short words back where they belong and save the magazine from disaster?

SOLUTION ON PAGE 176.

Film Fun (?)

Very often it is the catchy title of a film which makes it a box office sensation. There are many films which might have been famous except for a flaw in the title.

Can you name them from these brief outlines of their plots?

The final test match at Lords. A batsman has survived several calls for leg before wicket and is playing very slowly and boring everybody.

He eventually hits the ball hard and straight. No fielder touches the ball but suddenly it flies back and hits the batsman on the nose.

After years and years standing in salt water the piles of Bournemouth Pier have become soft and supple.

One night the pier becomes alive, tries its legs and walks out to sea!

After many adventures under the oceans of the world it comes back home again.

It is St David's Day, 1942. A convoy of 10 ships, each carrying 2,000 Welshmen returning to the land of their fathers after years in America, is ploughing across the ocean.

It is attacked by a German submarine and all the ships are sunk, with the loss of all the men.

At the children's birthday party all is laughter and fun – especially when a rather severe-looking nanny produces a hatpin and bursts all the balloons.

The Film of the Film!
A British spy escapes from the Kremlin with a handy object which is urgently needed at Shepperton Studios where the making of another Bond film is held up due to Arctic conditions.

(As well as the film title from this story, what film was being made at Shepperton?)

SOLUTION ON PAGE 175.

What Is It? (?)

There are those who think that it is flat
Though most think it is round.
To be closer still, it's tangerine-shaped
And on it you can be drowned!

What's Yours? (?)

Some keep theirs in the garden.
Some have theirs indoors.
Some are found under water.
Tell me – have you made yours?

The Place To Be (?)

My first is in fat but not in thin.
My next in wide but not in trim.
My third in old but not in young.
My fourth and fifth in large not small.
My sixth (and seventh!) in noise and sound.
My whole the place where you may be found.

A Word From The Bard (?)

First, it runs through field and town,
Never goes up, always goes down.
Then lifts and falls for many a day
'Til it climbs to the sky up, up and away.
It floats on high and puts on weight
Then falls once more at quite a rate.
When hot it's thin; when cold its hard.
So what is the subject of this bard?

Spot This One (?)

What has 21 spots but isn't ill?

Get This (?)

What's full of holes and gets hit with clubs?

SOLUTIONS ON PAGE 175.

Bleep, Bleep (?)

What's empty and tears round and round going 'bleep, bleep, fire! Bleep, bleep, fire!'?

Across The Great Divide (??)

Spare, if you will, a thought for Edwina Proud
Who now strums a harp on a heavenly cloud.
She died, at peace, on a recent Monday
But was laid in her grave on the PREVIOUS Sunday!

No crime or error attended this act.
So can you explain the incredible fact
That the lady died at half past four
And then was buried the day before?!

Codesquare (??)

The letters of the alphabet have been scattered about and cast forth upon the numbers 1 to 9. Thus the number 1 in the picture on the right can be either N, D or I. In the square, the same number always stands for the same letter so, like the ancient mariner who picketh one in three, can you find out which number stands for which letter and complete the word square with five words reading the same across and down?

1 D I N	**2** E C Q
3 T V P	**4** W U S
5 M G B	**6** A Y F
7 K L J	**8** Z R H
9 X O	

SOLUTIONS ON PAGE 175.

4	3	6	8	3
3	2	1	9	8
6	1	5	7	2
8	9	7	2	4
3	8	2	4	4

Codeword (???)

It may not look much like it but the picture overleaf really is a crossword grid. There are words going across and down and blank squares scattered here, there and probably somewhere else as well. All we have done is to replace the letters by a number and you can see that each number is shared by 2 letters. So the number 1 may be a or it may be b (try saying that ten times quickly!).

The blank has been coded by one of the numbers as well – and every blank does at least have the same number.

In case this looks harder than it really is, don't forget that after every word which does not end at the edge of the grid is a blank square. There must also be a blank square before each word which does not start at an edge.

SOLUTION ON PAGE 176.

Given all that help, can you now put each of the following words into its one correct position?

ABBA ACE ADDED AGE AHEAD BAD BADGE BEACH BEECH CADGE CHAFE CHEF DACE DEAF DECIDE DEFACE DI EACH EGG EH FACE FED FEE FIG HA HAD HEED HI IBID IDE IE IF JABBED JADE

2	3	3	1	2	3	4	4	5	1	5	2
3	4	3	4	1	4	3	1	2	4	4	4
1	2	2	3	2	4	4	1	3	1	2	4
3	4	4	1	4	3	4	1	4	4	4	1
4	3	1	2	3	4	5	1	1	1	3	2
4	5	4	4	4	4	1	4	3	4	3	4
3	4	4	4	1	1	2	4	3	4	4	3
3	4	4	2	1	2	3	4	2	4	5	3
2	3	2	5	2	3	4	2	4	1	3	3

1 = A or B
2 = C or D
3 = E or F
4 = G or H
5 = I or J

SOLUTION ON PAGE 175.

WHO DID WHAT?

Can you put the separate statements together and make the right deduction? For example . . . Henry drove the red car. The yellow van went over the cliff . . . So Henry, whatever fate befell him, did not make that long fall into the sea. Once you have found who didn't do what, you will discover who did. If using the grids is new to you, the chapter opens with a sample which is worked through completely to help you follow the method.

Stand in a load of stolen cement.

Have you done a Who Did What-type puzzle before? If so, turn to page 53. If not, read on. Here is the problem:

Five youngsters each played a different game on five different arcade machines. They scored five different totals as well but all we can recall is that

1. Teresa played Crunch and scored more than 5,000 but did not get the top score.
2. A boy played on the Marvel and a girl scored 6,000 playing Splat on the Quasar.
3. Thud was played on the Pinball.
4. Peter did not score as high as 10,000 which was made on the Wizard.
5. Phillip played Zap and he did not score less than 6,000.
6. Pow was not played by Steven and did not produce the lowest score.
7. The highest score was made on the Freakout.

The puzzle is to work out who played which game on which machine for how many points.

You could put all the facts together in your brain and let it churn around until, hopefully, it coughs up the answer like a Try Your Weight machine at the seaside. If all it does is make your head ache, then our grid may prove helpful.

It shows all the possible combinations which the puzzle throws up and can be filled in by putting a tick where a pair is proved to go together and a cross when the pairing is not possible.

As the grid is filled in, other facts will emerge like the cork out of a bottle of shaken champagne.

	Zap	Pow	Thud	Crunch	Splat	Quasar	Wizard	Pinball	Freakout	Marvel	3000	5000	6000	10 000	12 000
Alison				X_1											
Peter				X_1											
Teresa	X_1	X_1	X_1	$\checkmark_1$	X_1						X_1	X_1			X_1
Phillip				X_1											
Steven				X_1											
Quasar															
Wizard															
Pinball															
Freakout															
Marvel															
3000				X_1											
5000				X_1											
6000															
10 000															
12 000				X_1											

Clue 1: Put a tick for Teresa playing Crunch and a cross for all the others not playing that game. Teresa/Crunch has a score greater than 5,000 but not the top score, so put a cross for that score and less and a cross against 12,000, the top score.

	Zap	Pow	Thud	Crunch	Splat	Quasar	Wizard	Pinball	Freakout	Marvel	3000	5000	6000	10 000	12 000
Alison	X_2	X_2	X_2	X	$\checkmark_2$	$\checkmark_2$	X_2	X_2	X_2	X_2	X_2	X_2	$\checkmark_2$	X_2	X_2
Peter				X	X_2	X_2							X_2	X_2	
Teresa	X	X	X	✓	X	X_2				X_2	X	X	X_2	$\checkmark_2$	X
Phillip				X	X_2	X_2							X_2	X_2	
Steven				X	X_2	X_2							X_2	X_2	
Quasar	X_2	X_2	X_2	X_2	$\checkmark_2$										
Wizard					X_2										
Pinball					X_2										
Freakout					X_2										
Marvel				X_2	X_2										
3000				X	X_2										
5000				X	X_2										
6000	X_2	X_2	X_2	X_2	$\checkmark_2$										
10 000	X_2	X_2	X_2	$\checkmark_2$	X_2										
12 000				X	X_2										

Clue 2: A boy played on the Marvel so put a cross against each girl and the Marvel. From clue 1 we know a girl played Crunch so put a cross against Crunch/Marvel. A girl played Splat giving a cross against each boy and that game. This only leaves Alison, so she played Splat – a tick for that. It was played on the Quasar, so tick (and consequent crosses) record that fact. From this Teresa is only left with one possible score, 10,000, so tick that.

	Zap	Pow	Thud	Crunch	Splat	Quasar	Wizard	Pinball	Freakout	Marvel	3000	5000	6000	10 000	12 000
Alison	X	X	X	X	✓	✓	X	X	X	X	X	X	✓	X	X
Peter				X	X	X	X_4						X	X	X_4
Teresa	X	X	X	✓	X	X	$✓_4$	X_3	X_4	X	X	X	X	✓	X
Phillip				X	X	X	X_4						X	X	
Steven				X	X	X	X_4						X	X	
Quasar	X	X	X	X	✓										
Wizard	X_4	X_4	X_3	$✓_4$	X										
Pinball	X_3	X_3	$✓_3$	X_3	X										
Freakout			X_3	X_4	X										
Marvel			X_3	X	X										
3000				X	X										
5000				X	X										
6000	X	X	X	X	✓										
10 000	X	X	X	✓	X										
12 000				X	X										

Clue 3: Tick Thud/Pinball and cross the impossibles. Teresa did not play Thud, so put a cross against Teresa/Pinball.
Clue 4: Cross out Peter/12,000. Teresa is known already to have scored 10,000, so she played on the Wizard.

	Zap	Pow	Thud	Crunch	Splat	Quasar	Wizard	Pinball	Freakout	Marvel	3000	5000	6000	10 000	12 000
Alison	X	X	X	X	✓	✓	X	X	X	X	X	X	✓	X	X
Peter	X$_5$	✓$_6$	X$_6$	X	X	X	X	X$_6$	X$_7$	✓$_7$	X$_6$	✓$_6$	X	X	X
Teresa	X	X	X	✓	X	X	X	X	X	X	X	X	X	✓	X
Phillip	✓$_5$	X$_5$	X$_5$	X	X	X	X	X$_5$	✓$_7$	X$_7$	X$_5$	X$_5$	X	X	✓$_5$
Steven	X$_5$	X$_6$	✓$_6$	X	X	X	X	✓$_6$	X$_6$	X$_6$	✓$_6$	X$_6$	✓	X	X$_5$
Quasar	X	X	X	X	✓										
Wizard	X	X	X	✓	X										
Pinball	X	X	✓	X	X										
Freakout			X	X	X										
Marvel			X	X	X										
3000	X$_5$			X	X										
5000	X$_5$			X	X										
6000	X	X	X	X	✓										
10 000	X	X	X	✓	X										
12 000	✓$_5$	X$_5$	X$_5$	X	X										

Clue 5: Tick Phillip/Zap. Cross out Phillip scoring less than 6,000. This only leaves him with 12,000, so tick that. Phillip, by clue 3, could not have played on the Pinball, so cross that out.
Clue 6: Pow was not played by Steven, so that is crossed out and this only leaves him with Thud so tick that, and it is already known that that was played on the Pinball – another tick. This leaves Peter Playing Pow. He did not get the lowest score, so he scored 5,000 which leaves only Steven with 3,000.

Clue 7: Phillip was playing on the Freakout as he made the highest score. All of which leaves Peter on the Marvel and the solution is complete.

Alison	Splat	Quasar	6,000
Peter	Pow	Marvel	5,000
Teresa	Crunch	Wizard	10,000
Phillip	Zap	Freakout	12,000
Steven	Thud	Pinball	3,000

A snake and pygmy pie.

The Seaside Saga (?)

So excited were the four children on their way home on the coach that they chattered nonstop about their excursion to Sheermouth.

When the last had been dropped off, tiredly clutching the hand of the grown up who had taken him, the driver parked his coach and went home to tell his wife what a day they had all had.

She, naturally, wanted all the details but, being a good driver, he had concentrated on the road and could only remember a few snatches of conversation.

He knew that each child had had one special treat and had been with only one adult. He also remembered that:

The uncle had paid for the donkey ride.

Brian had eaten the ice cream, which a man had bought for him.

Tim did not go to the funfair and Sarah did not go on the donkey ride or with her aunt.

Mother took her daughter to the funfair while Tim went with his aunt.

The driver's wife tried to work out just which of the children had enjoyed which treat with which adult, but she became muddled and gave up.

Can you sort it out for her using the grid on the next page?

	Donkey Ride	Ice Cream	Funfair	Pier	Mother	Grandad	Uncle	Aunt
Sarah								
Brian								
Tim								
Joan								
Mother								
Grandad								
Uncle								
Aunt								

Name	Treat	Who with
Sarah		
Brian		
Tim		
Joan		

Minor League (?)

For the local correspondent of the *Much Squelching Argus and Ferret Gazette*, reporting the new basketball league which had sprung up in the village hall proved an unrewarding task.

Due more to lack of skill on the part of the exuberant youngsters rather than actual malice, he found himself involved in the game as ball-catcher, usually on the tip of the nose. The excited yelling of

SOLUTION ON PAGE 176.

four teams of youngsters, whose one ambition in life was to become seven feet tall, was a far cry from the weddings and council meetings which were his usual function.

Late that night, as he nursed two eyes which refused to work as a team, he tried to make some sense of his notes on the season just ended.

Bill's team finished higher in the league than Tony's team and the Allstars.

Leslie's team finished third.

Bluesox finished bottom of the league.

Fred played for the Giants who came second.

Can you give him a mental hand and list the four teams, their star player and where each finished the season?

	Allstars	Giants	Bluesox	Bears	1	2	3	4
Bill								
Fred								
Leslie								
Tony								
1								
2								
3								
4								

Name	Team	Position
Bill		
Fred		
Leslie		
Tony		

SOLUTION ON PAGE 176.

Ring O Rose's (?)

This delightful snap taken at the Happyhour Playgroup just before the ice cream and cakes started flying shows six children standing with their best friend on one side and their sibling on the other. (Sibling is a lovely word which means brother or sister – if you happen to have one under six months old it is your dribbling sibling!)

Now Colin's friend's brother is Edward.
Edward's friend is not Sarah.
Rose's brother's friend is Edward's sister.

Can you work out who is next to whom and so write each toddler's name by their picture?

Girls: Rose, Sarah, Tanya
Boys: Andrew, Colin, Edward

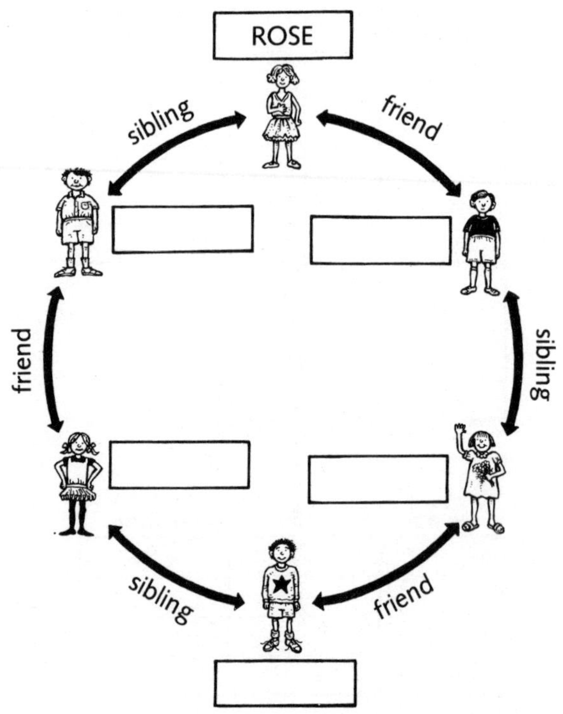

SOLUTION ON PAGE 177.

Fruit & Veg. (?)

For young Ted the youth opportunity scheme meant little more than humping great bags of potatoes around and constantly rearranging the display to suit the everchanging demands of his boss, Mr Squashett.

Ted's latest task is to present six fruits and six vegetables in a stand of three rows.

Old Squashie's commands were that fruit and veg. were to alternate across and down so that two fruits or two vegetables were never next to each other.

The oranges were to be directly above the cucumbers which were to be on the left of the grapes.

The sprouts must be above the pears; the plums directly above the cabbage and the apples in between the lettuce and the sprouts.

The cucumbers were to be in the bottom row on the right of the peaches.

The potatoes were to be in the bottom right corner, in the same column as the sprouts.

So just where did Ted put the carrots?

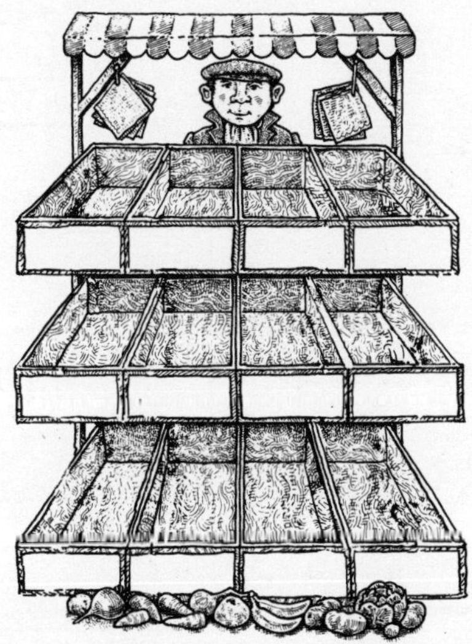

SOLUTION ON PAGE 177.

Road Up (?)

The Merrivale traffic census did a splendid job in proving what is known already, that there are too many cars using too few roads.

What they failed to record was who lived in which road but the record does show that:

The Sangsters went down as many roads as the Hughes' to reach the High Street.

Miss Briscoe used Fuller Vale to reach the High Street but the Dennetts' journey did not take them this way.

Mr Adams went down more roads to reach the High Street than Mrs Ready who went down more roads than Mr & Mrs Thomas, who lived in Fairfield Road.

Miss Briscoe turned right to leave the road she lived in, then right again to reach Mrs Ready's house which is in the next road to the Hughes family.

Can you complete the census form – posterity may need it!

(The number by each house in our helpful map gives the number of roads used to reach the High Street from each house.)

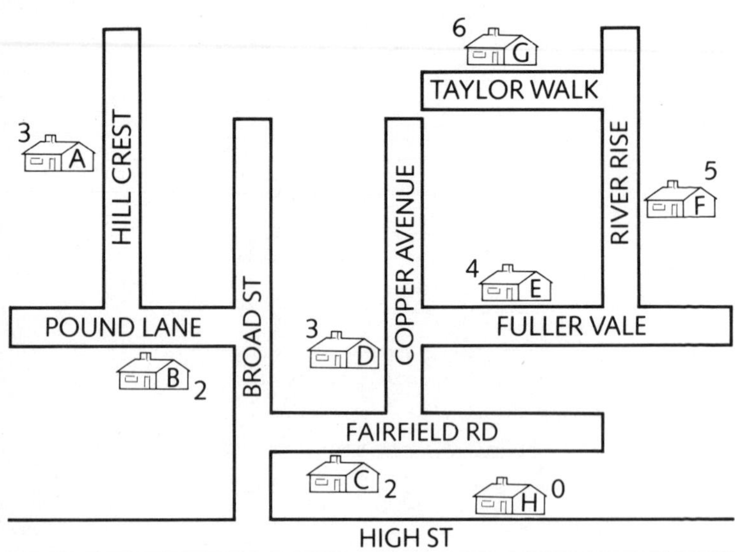

SOLUTION ON PAGE 176.

	A	B	C	D	E	F	G	H
Adams								
Briscoe								
Dennett								
Flower								
Hughes								
Ready								
Sangster								
Thomas								

A level crossing. When open to the traffic it is closed to the train and vice versa. (Also, country dwellers, a kissing gate is acceptable).

Take It From Here (??)

It was a mistake, the residents of Carrington Crescent later agreed, to let young Tim earn extra pocket money by sending him with a block order for five dinners to the Chinese takeaway in the High Street. Not that he disappeared with the money or dropped the order over the canal bridge on his way back. It was simply that between his forgetfulness and the shop owner's limited command of English, the result was one large and very mixed packet of foodstuffs and an order form sinking for the third time in a sea of sweet and sour sauce. As he dived, unseen, into the garage of Number 3, he had his facts as tangled as a plate of spaghetti.

Dora Innis had ordered number 21 and Mr Goldsmith wanted the special.

Charles, whose surname isn't Hooper, did not ask for number 45, the chop suey.

The chow mein, number 34, was ordered by Alice.

Number 52, the prawn rice, was the request of Ms Farley and not, as he had just guessed, Bill Jackson.

Can you save the young lad's bacon by refreshing his memory as to which person ordered what?

Their love was in vein (in vain!)

	Farley	Goldsmith	Hooper	Innis	Jackson	Foo Young	Chop Suey	Chow Mein	Prawn Rice	Special	16	21	34	45	52
Alice															
Bill															
Charles															
Dora															
Eileen															
Foo Young															
Chop Suey															
Chow Mein															
Prawn Rice															
Special															
16															
21															
34															
45															
52															

First Name	Surname	Dish	Number
Alice			
Bill			
Charles			
Dora			
Eileen			

SOLUTION ON PAGE 178.

Flash Crash (??)

KEITH: Now, on Saturday Sportshow we take you back live to Ballybrakedown for the latest report on the Irish Grand Prix – over to *you*, Moray.

MORAY: And the excitement here is – *tremendous*. All sorts of things happening since you were last with us. Now there are only five cars left in the race and I want to tell you that:

Fire put young Chappell out of the race and fans of Max will be disappointed to hear that he didn't finish, after hitting a patch of oil in his Flash.

Clive drove the Streak and the Lightning caught fire.

Steve Quest was taken to hospital, though we are pleased to say he wasn't badly hurt, after losing the bend.

Morelli ran out of fuel and Phil Davies drove the Zoom.

Over to you, Keith, in the studio.

KEITH: I make that four cars out of the last five have each suffered a different disaster – so WHO WON?

MORAY: Sorry, Keith, can't hear you.

KEITH: Listeners, we seem to have lost the line to Ireland – so we'll have to ask you to tell us who won and what car he was driving.

In hospital, of course, in wards 5, 6, 7 and 8.

	Bennett	Chappell	Davies	Morelli	Quest	Flash	Jet	Lightning	Streak	Zoom	WINNER	Fire	Lost Bend	No Fuel	Oil Patch
Clive															
John															
Max															
Phil															
Steve															
Flash															
Jet															
Lightning															
Streak															
Zoom															
WINNER															
Fire															
Lost Bend															
No Fuel															
Oil Patch															

First Name	Surname	Car	Event
Clive			
John			
Max			
Phil			
Steve			

SOLUTION ON PAGE 177.

Daylight Robbery (???)

It was unfortunate for Constable Paynting that he was on traffic duty at the town roundabout just as a daring robbery took place along West Way. The escaping criminal headed in his direction and transferred the swag under his very nose to a van which the accomplice drove away.

It being a hot and sultry afternoon the policeman was beset with the problem of deciding whether to wave the traffic along, thus making a pleasant breeze waft around his face or keep completely still and so reduce the perspiration each little movement caused. So preoccupied was he that his later report to the superintendent is a model of confusion.

Nobody entered and left the roundabout by the same road.

The driver of the van, who wasn't Mr Wilkins, passed two exits before turning off, and that was not along West Way.

The lady driver of the Mini arrived at the roundabout along Knoyle View but did not exit along the High Street, where the sports car went.

The saloon came from Bradley Road and Mr Lomond from the High Street.

The estate driver left by the road Miss Hammett arrived along, which wasn't Long Lane.

Neither Mrs Green nor the lady in the sports car used Bradley Road at all but the driver of the Mini did.

Can you save the constable's career by quickly slipping him the names of the two criminals involved, the cars they used and the roads they arrived and left by?

A similar list of the other road users will help establish their innocence.

Rainbow.

		Mini	Van	Saloon	Sports	Estate	Approach: High St	Approach: Long Lane	Approach: Bradley Rd	Approach: Knoyle View	Approach: West Way	Exit: High St	Exit: Long Lane	Exit: Bradley Rd	Exit: Knoyle View	Exit: West Way
	Mr Lomond															
	Miss Hammett															
	Mrs Green															
	Mr Wilkins															
	Miss Lever															
Approach	High St															
Approach	Long Lane															
Approach	Bradley Rd															
Approach	Knoyle View															
Approach	West Way															
Exit	High St						X									
Exit	Long Lane							X								
Exit	Bradley Rd								X							
Exit	Knoyle View									X						
Exit	West Way										X					

Name	Car	Approach	Exit
Mr Lomond			
Miss Hammett			
Mrs Green			
Mr Wilkins			
Miss Lever			

SOLUTION ON PAGE 177.

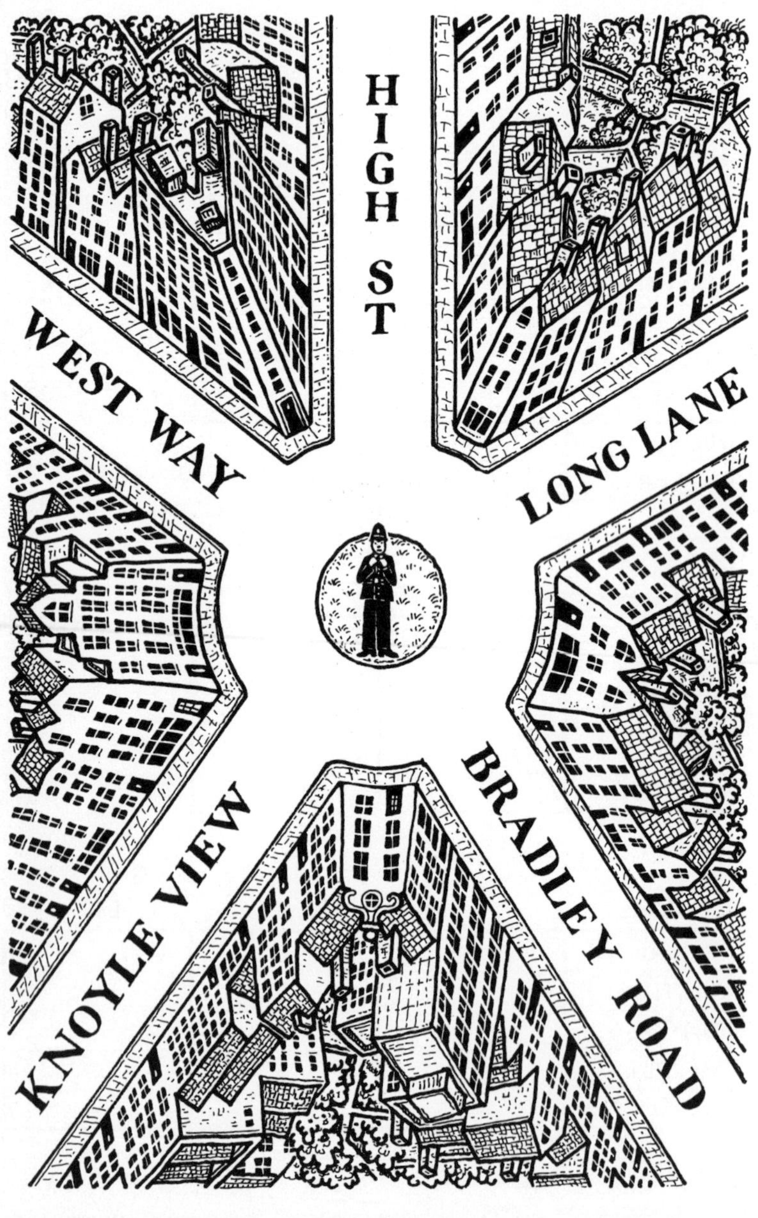
HIGH ST
WEST WAY
LONG LANE
KNOYLE VIEW
BRADLEY ROAD

AMAZING MAZES

Threading a maze is a popular pastime which has deep roots in both our religious and leisure past. In these mazes, though, you are not simply asked to make your way from A to B, but to take part in a mental steeplechase which has a variety of hidden hurdles. In some, you won't know your Up from your Down until symbols are decoded; in others you will try to retrace the path taken by a drunken ant after it unwittingly wandered through a puddle of best bitter.

The Marsh Of Mynog (?)

There is very little crime in the forests of Mynog, mainly because the inhabitants are too small to get up to much and the fearsome marsh contains creatures nasty enough to frighten anything into being good.

Also, the Mynogians discovered long ago that a guilty person becomes so obsessed with their dark secret that they cannot concentrate on even simple tasks, such as counting 1, 2, 3, 1, 2, 3, 1 . . .

Which is why, when they have to have a trial in Mynog, the supposed criminal is made to go through the dreaded marsh by jumping from stepping stone to stepping stone in correct order, 1, 2, 3, 1 . . .

They are only just big enough to jump from a stone to one of its neighbours and as they jump off a stone it disappears below the soggy, squelchy surface never to be seen, or used, again.

The mathematical marsh monsters keep a keen eye out for anyone breaking the rules and if someone does, GULP! then a crime is avenged.

Only an innocent person will be able to concentrate and find the one path through to freedom – can you?

Always. Year always begins with Y and end always begins with E.

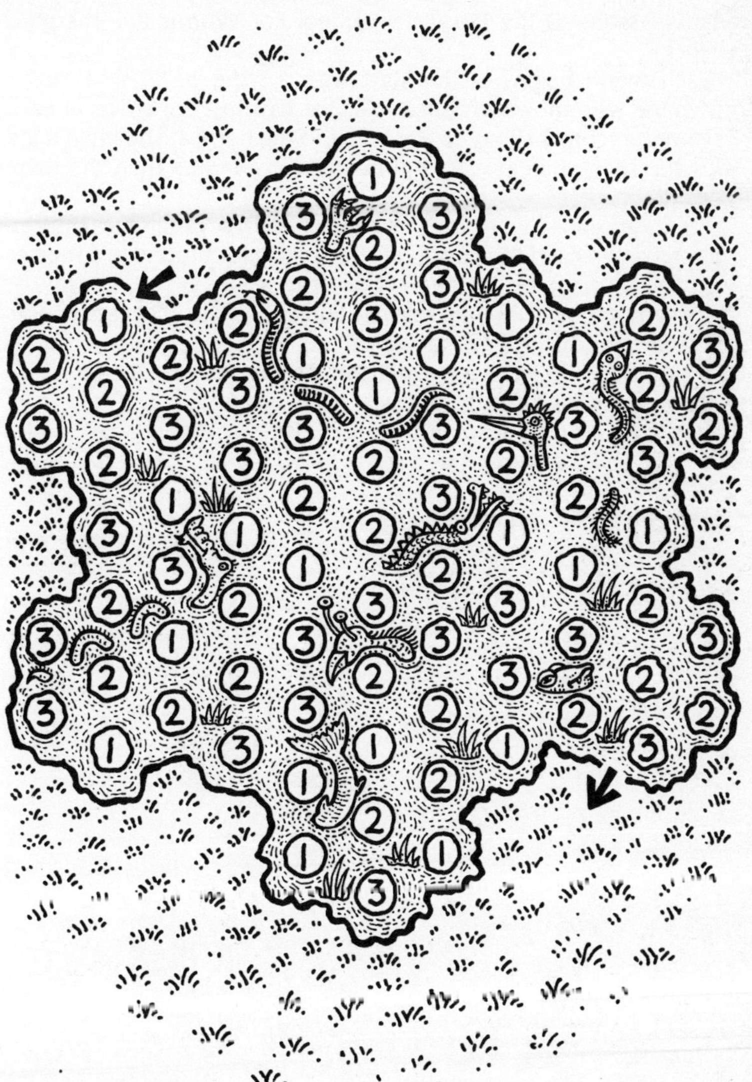

SOLUTION ON PAGE 179.

Sum Maze (?)

Maths lessons at the Dinglydell School For Worms are energetic events.

Each worm begins at the Start with a score of 10 and travels down the wormholes which connect the caverns. On arrival at each cavern the score is changed according to the number shown, if it is a *plus* the score increases by the number, if a *minus* then the score goes down.

On its journey a worm can visit each cavern several times but can only go down each tube once. It is too big to turn round in a tube as well and must go on to the next cavern.

As soon as the little chap reaches End the beetle in charge checks his score and off he goes for lunch.

If you were down there, what sort of score could you get?

Compare your effort to this worm's eye chart:

Below 20 : You're heading for the birds!
20 – 28 : Not good
29 – 38 : Not bad
39 – 48 : Now you are moving
over 48 : Excellent; go on to the next lesson – Black Holes And How To Dig Them.

Bees hum because they don't know the words of the song.

SOLUTION ON PAGE 182.

By the soap!

Clued Brick Cube (??)

Can you find the only route from start to end in this, the only version of the iniquitous cube which doesn't move or fly apart just at the time you are about to solve it? Each symbol has just one meaning – Up, Down, Right, or Left and they are arranged on the faces so that you can never, if you have the correct meaning, leave the surfaces you can see. Thus it is clear from the symbols above the starting square that neither circle nor triangle can mean left.

Given that, can you work out just which sign means what and find the only path?

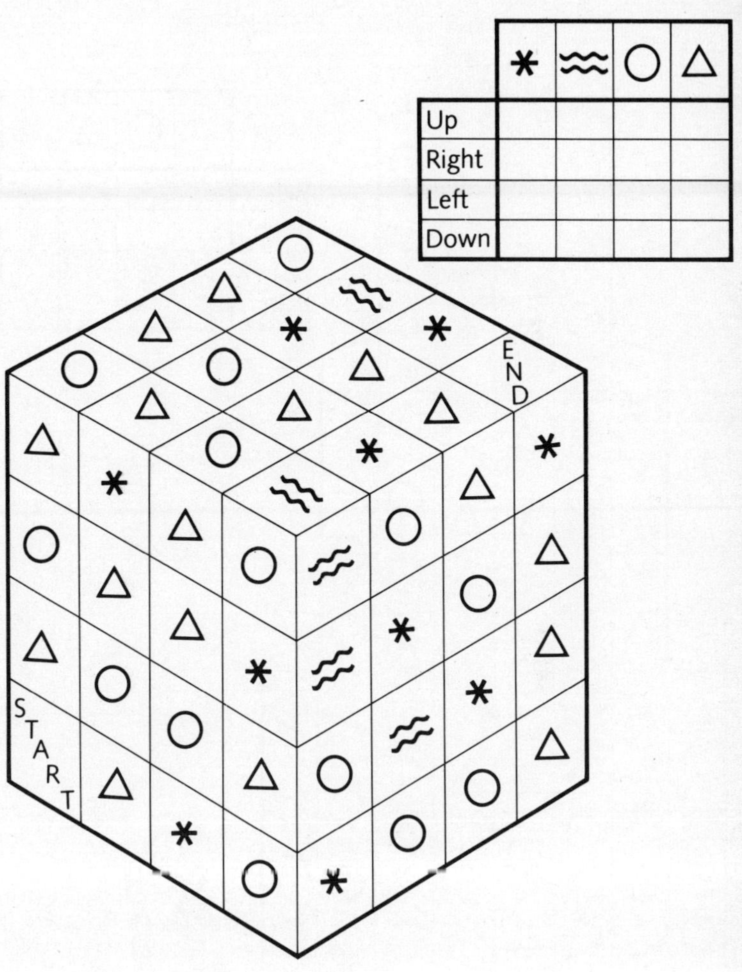

	✱	≈	○	△
Up				
Right				
Left				
Down				

SOLUTION ON PAGE 178.

SOLUTION ON PAGE 178.

Devine Intervention (??)

The dreaded Killer Mouse has trapped lovely Dolores Devine on top of Tottering Towers (see left). Her thin screams, battling against the roar of London traffic, are, fortunately, heard by the only man who can save her – Wally the window cleaner. With his magnetic hands he can inch from pane to pane and so reach the top, deal with the monster mouse and save the lovely girl – before popping off for a chip supper.

If, that is, he can find the one safe route to the top of the building.

Killer Mouse has worked his wicked ways and painted a design on each pane of glass. Each symbol has a different meaning – one stands for Up, another Down, a third Right and the fourth Left.

The snag is that if Wally makes a wrong move the glass will shatter, leaving him clinging fiercely to thin air, and we all know how unreliable that is as a means of support.

Wally, though a wonder at scaling without scaffolding, is a little short on grey matter – he can't work out which symbol means what, though he has realized that he can stroll anywhere along the ledges which separate each section of the building.

Can you give him a mental hand and tell him the meaning of each sign and thus mark out the only route to the top?

Red Riding Route (??)

Just in case you've ever wondered why the wolf had so much time to get to Grannie's, ask after her rheumatism, bung her in the cupboard, dress up in the old lady's nightwear and put on a full face of make-up before the little girl came tripping up the path, we can reveal that Red Riding Hood had more on her plate than a quick sprint across town.

From Home she had to visit, first, the shops and buy the goodies, next find her way to, and through, the woods (why she didn't heed her mother's advice and take the bus we'll never know) and finally meander about until she stumbled across the cottage of her aged relative.

Being a girl of simple mind she armed herself with a map riddled with numbers (see over). The number in each rectangle shows the distance she could travel Right, Left, Up or Down in a straight line only. A diagonal move was totally beyond her.

The rectangle she landed on then gave her a fresh number of rectangles to move over for the next leg of her journey.

She must visit the shops and the woods in that order and then move on to Grannie's by landing on each of those rectangles at the end of a move.

She must never land on or pass over any of the named rectangles at any time other than when they are being visited in their correct sequence.

If she is ever going to catch that wolf napping she'll have to break the secret of the maze and mark the route to Grannie's.

Can you do that for her?

HOME 1	1	5	4	3	3	1	6
0	1	0	1	2	2	3	4
3	5	4	1	SHOPS 1	2	0	4
0	1	1	0	4	2	1	1
2	WOODS 1	5	2	0	3	3	3
0	0	2	1	3	4	3	6
2	3	2	2	4	1	0	GRANNIE'S

The Drunken Ant (?, ?? & ???)

Amateur naturalist Edwin Plotts did not have to travel far to enjoy his hobby for halfway up his garden path was a crack in the concrete which served as the front door to a large, multi-storey ants' nest.

It was Edwin's custom after Sunday lunch to encamp on the path surrounded by the paraphernalia of his science – a notebook, pencil, sunglasses and a pint of beer.

His speciality was *antics* – those apparently random movements of the species as they crossed and recrossed the path and flower

SOLUTION ON PAGE 179.

borders. He was convinced that if he selected one specimen and followed it for long enough, plotting its movements on squared paper, he would learn the secret of its navigation. Each square on his grid represented a small patch of ground and he entered an arrow to show the direction the ant was travelling in at the time.

The result of Plott's work is somewhat spoiled by two unscientific factors in his study – the records became so messy that squares the ant visited more than once were a useless splodge without discernible directions and the ant he selected had just passed through a puddle of beer spilt when the deckchair collapsed.

As he tries to recreate the ant's path he knows that each square with one arrow in is a square the ant visited once only. Those squares which contain a star are places the ant visited more than once. Also Edwin does recall that the ant always went straight on or turned right or turned left; it never turned round to leave a square the same way it entered by.

He has little hope of untangling this mess and finding the exact route the ant took but would like his records to show a possible path.

Can you find a way the ant could have made its journey?

Give yourself a bonus pat on the back if you can discover a path which takes the insect through the squares the least number of times.

1. SUNDAY 7th AUGUST (?)

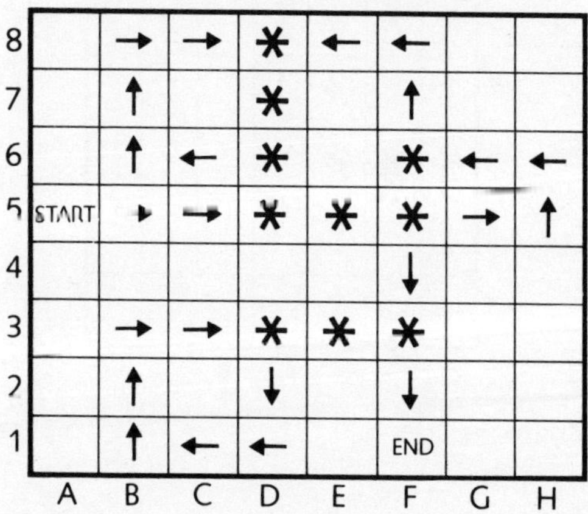

SOLUTION ON PAGE 180.

2. SUNDAY 14th AUGUST (?)

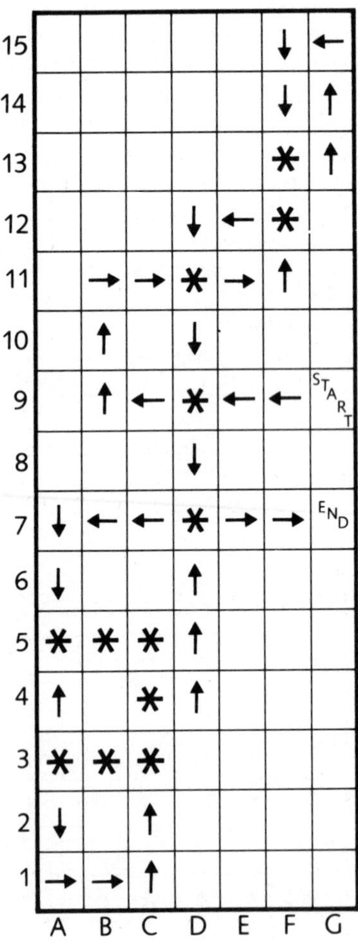

SOLUTION ON PAGE 180.

3. SUNDAY 21st AUGUST (??)

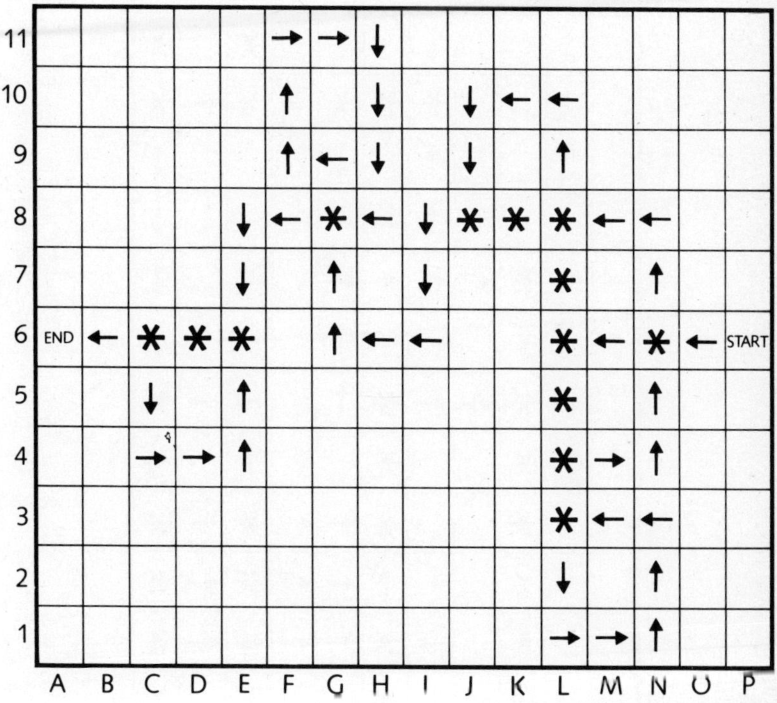

SOLUTION ON PAGE 181.

4. SUNDAY 28th AUGUST (???)

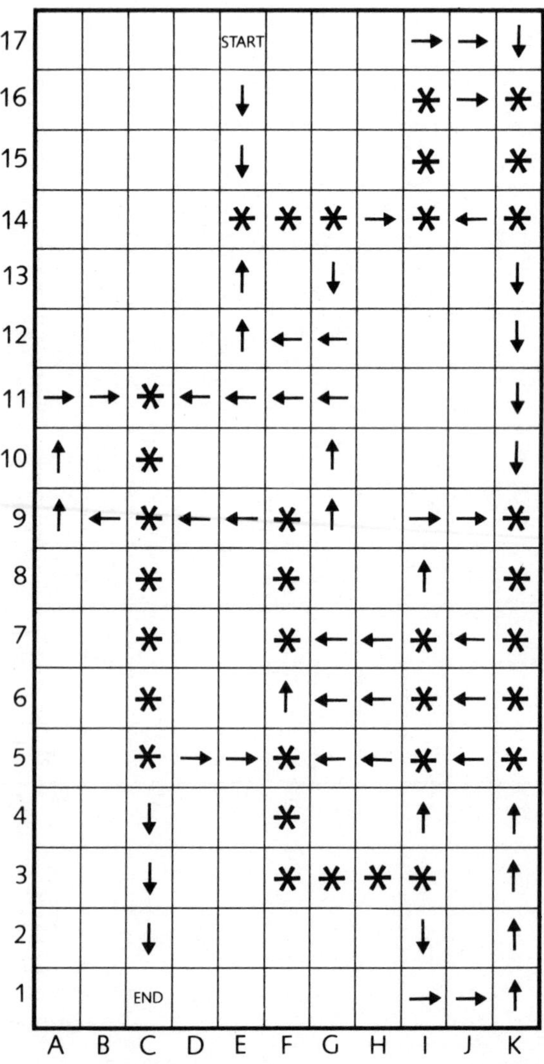

SOLUTION ON PAGE 181.

The Maze Phrase Of Philos (???)

Excavations by Sir Eustace Loffe at this site have thrown up fresh and startling theories on the life of the Ancient Greeks. The discovery of long, thin clay pots with narrow necks in what was probably a supermarket storeroom 30 feet below sea level has led Sir Eustace to suggest that the aqualung is much older than is generally supposed.

Controversial as this may be, the many clay tablets found at Philos provide much clearer evidence that many of our cherished sayings are not recorded accurately. For example, it is now known that the phrase 'It never rains but it pours' originated in a letter by Sossygenes to his mother written while he was travelling in Egypt. Referring to a wayward camel which would not submit to his control he wrote 'It never reins but it paws.'

The tablet shown overleaf is typical of the finds and shows one of the amusements the ancients enjoyed on the slopes below Olympus.

A phrase well known to them has been laid out on the slabs of a spiral pathway. Begin at START and move either three or five squares at each move to land on a letter. You may move backwards as well as forwards, though you cannot change direction in the middle of a move. If you find the correct sequence of moves the letters you land on will spell a word. After each word you must move to land on a star before starting the next word. Each letter in the spiral is only used once and the blanks are never landed on.

If you can find the hidden route then your path will spell out the original version of a well known saying before you reach END. What is it?

SOLUTION ON PAGE 182.

INITIATIVE TESTS

Can you spot patterns, make simple deductions or think laterally? If a straightforward connection doesn't immediately spring to mind, try taking a cockeyed look at the situation since, as you will no doubt soon discover, the author has a twisted, though fiendishly logical, view of life.

Missing Link (?)

Which of the four pictures, A, B, C, D, rightfully belongs in the empty space?

A

B

C

D

Ninewords (?)

In each grid opposite a nine-letter word has been rather carefully spread around. To find the word, first find the right place to start and then trace out a path from letter to letter by moving up, down, right, left or diagonally to the next square.

The words are all in common use and there is a clue to each should you need it.

SOLUTION ON PAGE 184.

1

A	M	A
L	R	M
A	D	E

On the break-fast table.

2

S	E	L
P	C	E
E	O	T

Far-seeing.

3

N	B	D
O	A	M
T	N	I

Indoor sport.

4

L	I	C
E	U	I
S	D	O

Very tasty.

5

E	N	G
I	X	P
R	O	L

Going places.

6

S	E	L
S	E	N
S	I	O

Without sound.

7

D	E	P
N	S	E
O	V	R

Get into debt.

8

Y	A	D
Y	S	R
E	E	T

It's in the past.

9

C	I	A
T	R	C
A	B	O

Very agile.

SOLUTION ON PAGE 184.

Jekyll & Hyde? (?)

Two famous TV stars are on this 'box' today, though the picture is rather scrambled! Can you switch to the right channel and say who they are?

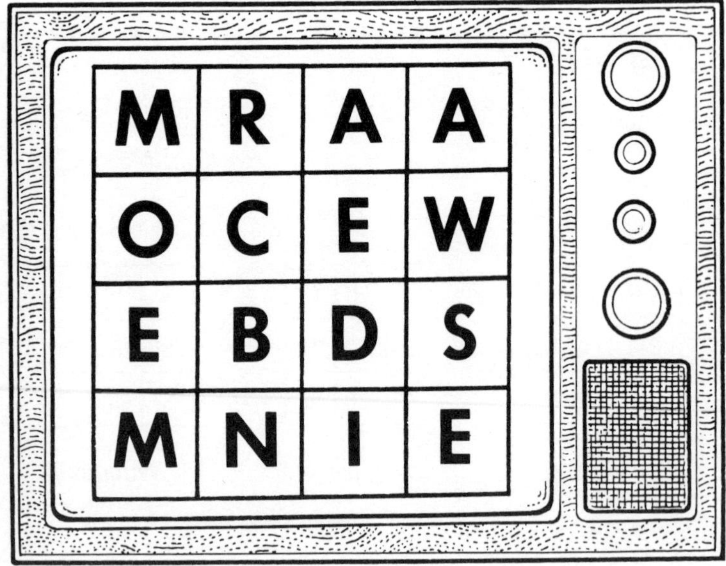

SOLUTION ON PAGE 184.

In The Picture (?)

One of the four pictures A, B, C, D, belongs in the empty space – can you work out which?

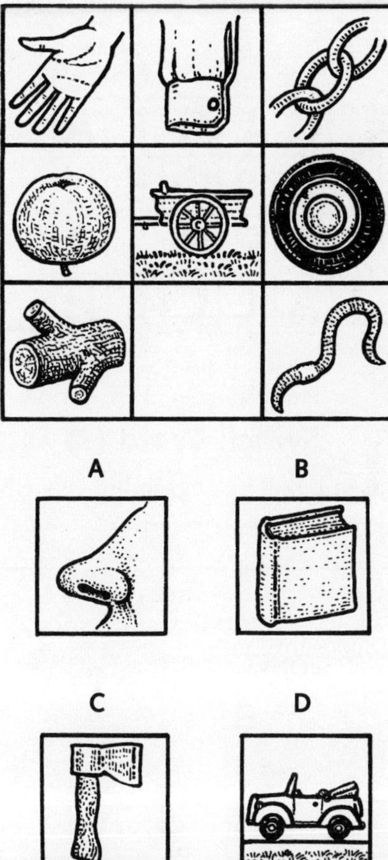

SOLUTION ON PAGE 184.

Fruit Salad (?)

Four different fruits, each a five-letter word, have been thoroughly mixed up in this bowl.

You could just list the letters and painfully make up the names of the four fruits but, thanks to the special power of our mixer, the parts have been very logically scattered.

Can you quickly sort out what has been done and so name the ingredients of this dish?

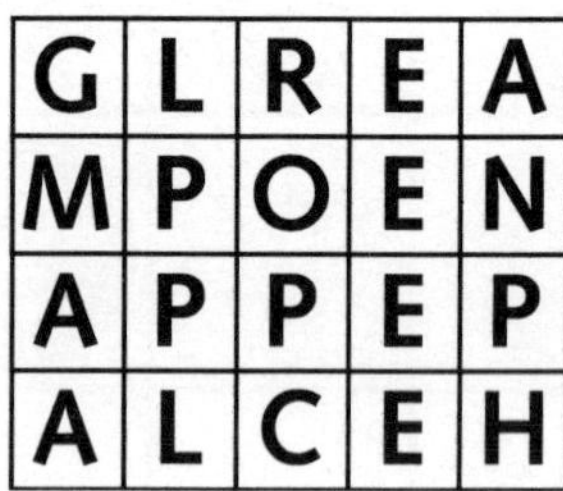

G	L	R	E	A
M	P	O	E	N
A	P	P	E	P
A	L	C	E	H

Switch Word (?)

One of the words in box B belongs in box A – which is it?

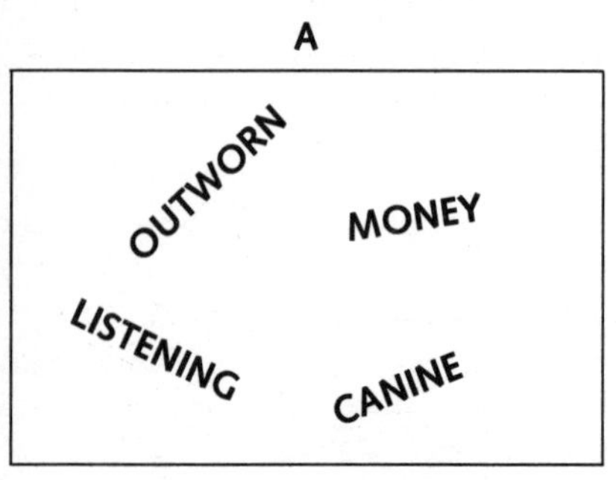

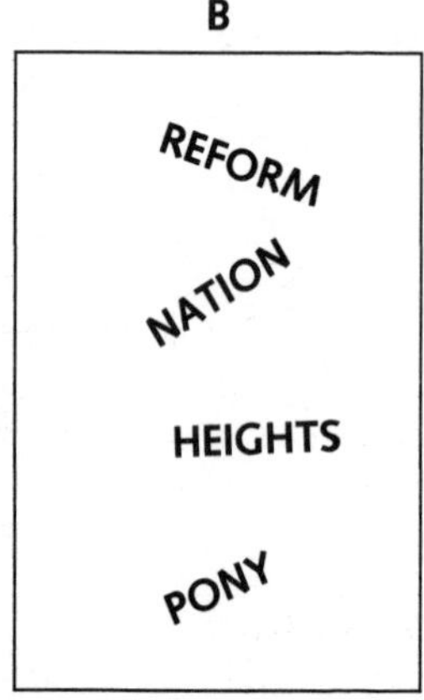

SOLUTIONS ON PAGE 183.

Time For The Bus (?)

What number should be on the bus which leaves the depot at 6.18?

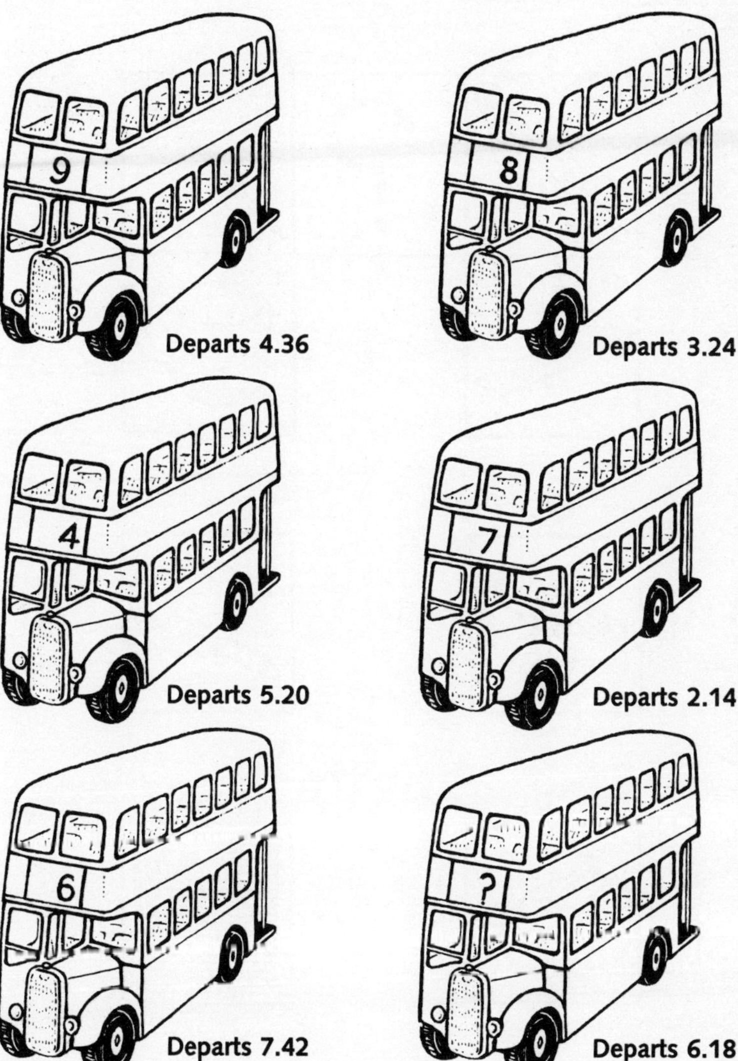

SOLUTION ON PAGE 183.

Pick A Pic (?)

Which of the pictures, A, B, C, D, belongs in box number two?

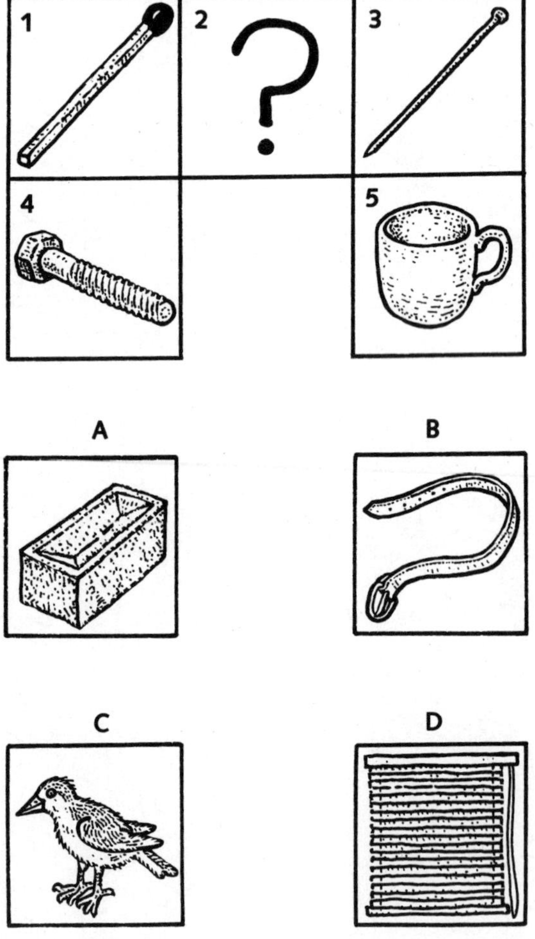

SOLUTION ON PAGE 183.

Links (?)

Which of the four pictures, A, B, C, D, fits into the empty space?

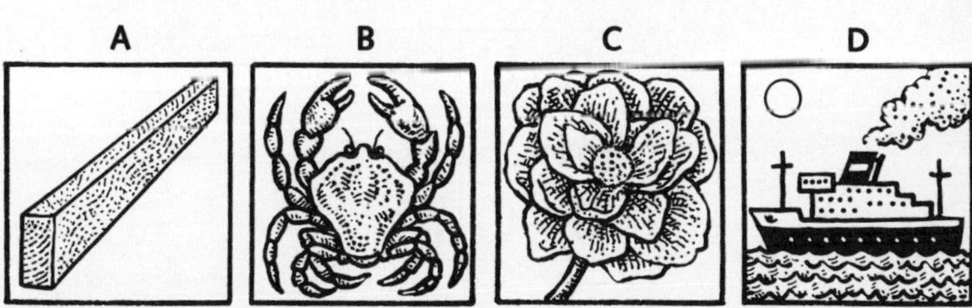

SOLUTION ON PAGE 183.

Missing Four (?)

It is probably obvious that C, F, L, M, are missing from this square, but where does each letter belong?

A	I	B	J
K			D
E			N
O	G	P	H

Number Please (?)

Which number belongs in the empty square?

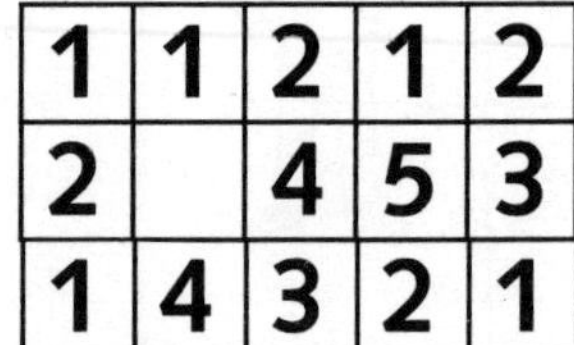

1	1	2	1	2
2		4	5	3
1	4	3	2	1

Don't Touch (?)

What letter is needed to complete this square?

O	U	D
R		A
E	G	N

SOLUTIONS ON PAGES 183 AND 184.

A fission chip shop.

Meet The Dealer (? & ??)

Among the many unsung heroes of the real wild west is a shadowy figure known simply as 'the dealer'.

He was never the stuff of which films would be made; he didn't carry a gun, nurture a civil war grudge for 20 years or save Wyatt Earp's life. And he died, peacefully, with his boots *off* in a hotel for retired gentlefolk.

Yet he left behind a legacy of tales, some true, some mythical, which will outlast any gunfight at the Not-So-Bad Corral.

Part of the aura which surrounded him whenever he travelled the frontier trails was caused by his hands which were were exceptionally clean and well-tended for those largely unwashed times.

They needed to be, for he could look at a pack of cards once and, with a quick riffle, deal any hand or the complete pack in any order he chose.

It was his enjoyment to lay out a spread of cards on the green baize with one card turned over and challenge his onlookers to name the hidden card correctly, there always being some logic to the layout. Mostly he did this for amusement, such as in the Seattle Square, designed purely for children. On some he accepted wagers as to the name of the card and would earn many a comfortable night's lodging from his puzzled gold diggers.

Three of his more famous hands are shown on the next two pages. If you had been with Zeke at the Malemute Saloon, could you be sure of making a winning bet?

Seattle Square (?)

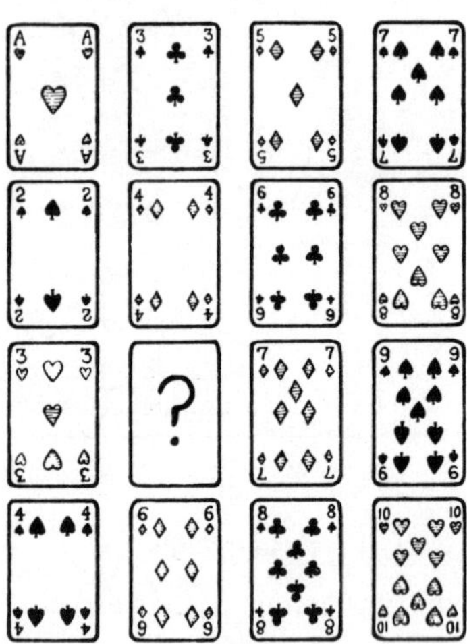

Denver Diamond (?)

SOLUTIONS ON PAGE 183.

Toledo Triangle (??)

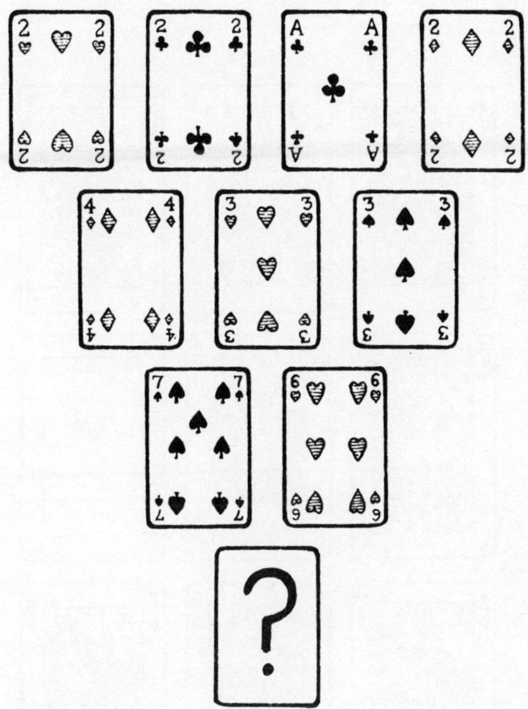

SOLUTION ON PAGE 184.

Get The Picture (??)

Just one of the four cards below the picture is the right one to complete it.
Which?

SOLUTION ON PAGE 183.

Cup Tied (??)

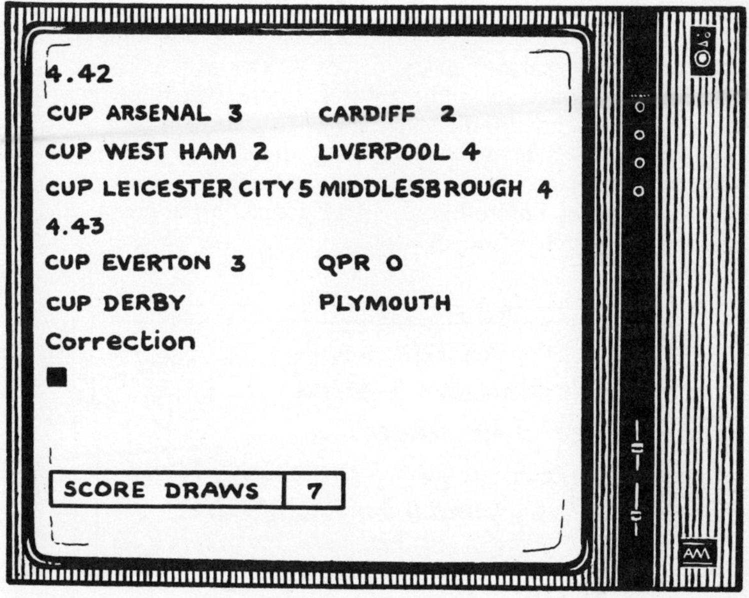

It was really too much for Bert when the operator of the teleprinter results service realized he had missed the goals off the last match and left the cursor blinking for what seemed an eternity.

It was even worse when the presenter of the programme cheerfully moved on to the horseracing results and left Bert with seven score draws and needing that one missing result to be a draw as well to win the jackpot he had dreamed of all his life.

Had he but known it, he could work out the result of that missing match from those on the screen above it – incredible as it may seem the scores are all logically determined.

Did Bert win the pools that week, or did he have to be satisfied with a smaller dividend?

SOLUTION ON PAGE 183.

Poetic Justice (??)

When the celebrated poet, Phineas Phearst, died at his country house it was fairly obvious to the local constable that his departure had not been a natural one.

The knife sticking out from the spot where Phineas normally kept his limp-bound notebook told Constable Paynting that here was his chance to show zeal and ability.

If only he could solve the mystery there would be enough feathers in his helmet to make him look like an ostrich on a bicycle.

The squad car's siren moaning along the distant drive told the officer that he had only a few moments to make the most of what little evidence lay before him: a list of people in the house at the time and Phearst's last poem.

Mrs. Dora Phearst ~ wife
Reggie Cornwallis ~ friend
Alice ~ housekeeper
Lord Peter da Quincy & his wife, Silvia
Thomas ~ companion/chauffeur
Morris Denham, publisher & his wife, Sadie

Lewis Carroll had A
Dream not once but every day.
She saw what I
Last left behind, slav
Impressions o'er the sea.

The ink of the poem was still damp – he had written his final masterpiece with his murderer in the room, perhaps taking a twisted delight in granting him a last favour.

It must contain the identity of the murderer, if only Paynting could spot it.

He couldn't. Can you?

SOLUTION ON PAGE 184.

WHODUNNIT?

This chapter takes you back to the logical land of law and order and lets you play detective in a variety of visual and verbal situations. There are grids to fill in with the aim of eliminating suspects, photofit pictures to study for the one revealing clue, and tangled tales from dubious characters who cloud the issue with a cunning combination of truth and falsehood.

Pic Fit (?)

Five lots of witnesses have very kindly assisted police in their enquires and, helped by the station artist, have produced photofit pictures of four villains (Pictures 1 to 5). However, each witness has one detail wrong.

From their offerings the police have created five more possible pictures of the criminals (Pictures A to E).

In each case, which picture should the police publish as being the correct likeness?

ONE – Video shop break-in

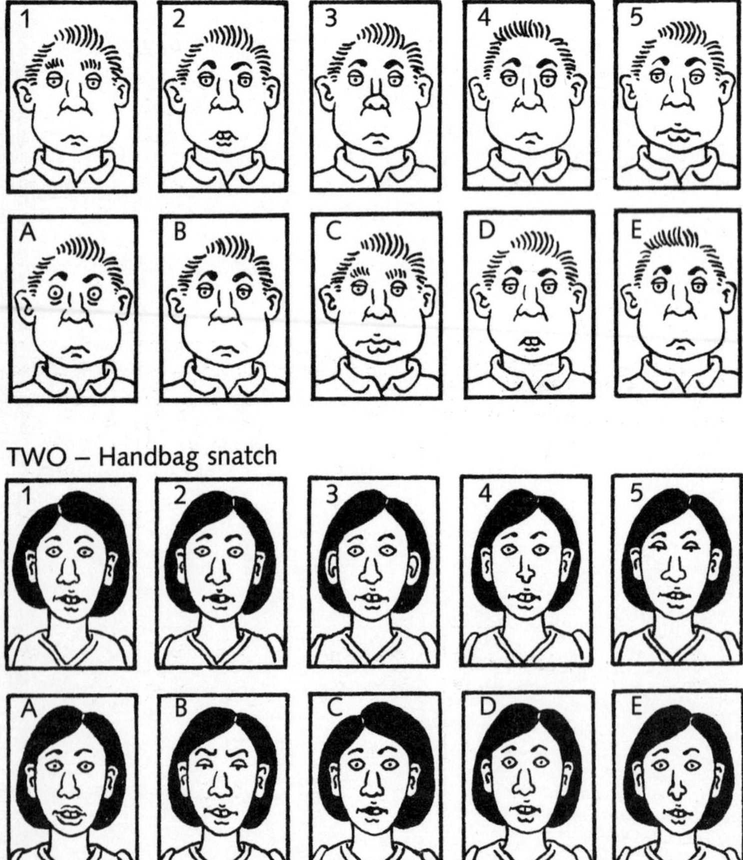

SOLUTIONS ON PAGE 185.

THREE – Shoplifting

1

2

3

4

5

A

B

C

D

E

FOUR – Vandalism

1

2

3

4

5

A

B

C

D

E

SOLUTIONS ON PAGE 185.

Victory On Paper (?)

As is often the case with local newspapers, the lavish interviews and photo sessions which give the participants the notion of a double page spread usually end up as a single picture and the wrong caption tucked somewhere between the fatstock prices and the council meeting reports.

Such was the case of the Hotel Europa's Grand Seaside Sports Tournament. Not a word was printed until the contestants had been reduced to the last four and then only a single picture of the tennis tournament with no caption. Which left the locals wondering what was going on. The two lines of text below the picture of the cricket contest shown the next week were a little more revealing but these two paled into insignificance when the final event, the golf contest, followed by the presentation of the trophy, was carefully captured for eternity *from behind*!

Could you just drop a line to the editor and tell him who won?

Brian Inglish receiving the first ball from Harry Scott while Colin Welsh keeps wicket and John Ireland waits for a catch.

SOLUTION ON PAGE 185.

The Long Shot (?)

When Alphonse Clotheade and Gaston Mugginge decided that only a duel could sort out their Gallic differences they chose modern weapons for the purpose. Early one morning they climbed a deserted nearby Alp and set off after each other with high-powered rifles equipped with telescopic sights and every modern hunting aid except radar, infra-red and silencers.

The only witness, Philip de Phluter, said later that he was talking to Gaston when the latter suddenly broke off, ran a few paces and raised his gun. Although Philip only heard one shot, Gaston fell dead nearly at his feet and later he found Alphonse, seriously wounded, on a small hillock two thousand metres away. When Alphonse was brought before the court on a charge of murder he pleaded guilty to manslaughter on the grounds of self-defence. His council, asked to explain this plea, stated that his client had fired after being fired upon and therefore could claim that he fired in self-defence.

It all depends on who fired first, so did Alphonse get away with the lesser charge or was he convicted of murder?

Open And Shut Case (?)

Using the new technology, Interpol have wired Scotland Yard that a spy carrying stolen documents is heading for Heathrow. They have managed to take a picture of him as he left Orly Airport.

SOLUTION ON PAGE 185.

The information was rapidly passed to detectives at the airport but they were hampered by the number of similar men carrying similar cases all getting off the same plane.

Which man should the detectives arrest and search?

SOLUTION ON PAGE 185.

Cromwell's Revenge (?)

It was at least an hour before dawn on the morning of the Battle at Edgehill when a sentry on duty rushed to Cromwell's HQ and demanded to see that great soldier at once.

He was so insistent that Cromwell heard the noise and agreed that he would listen to his story.

'General', the man said, 'I beg you to stay away from the field today.'

Cromwell laughed out loud at this extraordinary request.

'Why?' he asked.

'I have just had a terrible dream,' said the lookout, 'in which I saw a royalist cannon explode in front of you. The blast knocked you from your horse and you were dragged right through the enemy lines to a horrible death. It must be a portent from God on High. I had to warn you.'

Looking grave, but inwardly feeling amused, Cromwell dismissed the man with his thanks and continued his preparations for battle.

When the day was nearly over he asked one of his aides to find out if the soldier had survived the battle as easily as he himself had.

On being told that the man had not been hurt at all, the leader of the parliamentary cavalry immediately ordered his execution.

Why? What had he done to deserve such a fate?

Truth Will Out (??)

'Don't look so down, my boy,' the gang's leader said as the cell door closed behind them. 'Alright, so they caught us with the jewels but there weren't any witnesses at the scene so we're sitting pretty.'

'How do you make that out?' another asked.

'Look. They do us for possession but unless the prosecution can make it clear exactly what happened at the raid, they can't convict us for it.'

'So what do we do?' asked the third.

'We just mix our statements up; all lies and truth together. That way they'll never work out which of us did which part of the raid. One of us though, is a bad liar, so he'll tell the truth all the time.

SOLUTION ON PAGE 185.

One can get away with a fib now and again, so he tells one true fact and one lie.'

'And the other one?'

'He lies both times. Come here. I've written down what we'll say:

ALF	I drove the van.
	Bert threw the brick.
BERT	Charlie threw the brick.
	Alf drove the van.
CHARLIE	Bert waved the gun around.
	I drove the van.

Now memorize it. You'll see tomorrow, boys...'

'... and in conclusion,' said the judge, 'despite your efforts at subterfuge, it is clear what part each of you played in this raid and I will now pass sentence.'

Can you, like the judge, work out just who did what?[1]

1. I promise not to make a habit of these footnotes, I know how useless they usually are, telling you to read REX V SUGDEN 1792 or something. But just in case you find these puzzles a little hard to get cracking on, look up the solution to this one (pages 185 to 186) which will go into the matter pretty fully. This should then make the rest child's play. OK? Just thought I'd mention it.

Caught Napping (??)

It is surprising, really, that Sluffy's gang ever tried another kidnapping. The last time they did it the parents of a particularly repellent offspring had sent them a ransom note demanding payment if they returned the child!

This latest effort went sadly wrong as well – if you are going to climb in through a third floor bedroom window it is no use having a ladder just long enough to smash the glass on the second floor.

Having mixed with the criminal fraternity for long enough, they too hope to get away with dissembling, so when making their statements one tells the truth both times, one lies both times and one tries one of each variety. Though, in fact, each did one of the actions leading to the arrest.

SOLUTION ON PAGES 185 TO 186.

MUGSY I wrote the ransom note.
Sudsy climbed in the window.
PATSY Sudsy wrote the ransom note.
I set the ladder up.
SUDSY I climbed in the window.
Patsy wrote the note.

Can you work out what kind of truth-teller/liar each one is and so discover who had what function in that failed attempt?

Double Trouble (??)

Slugger blamed Toddy for the disaster and Ugly blamed both of them. What should have happened was that one would ram the mail van, one would spray the driver with a gas which would release him from all further interest in the proceedings and the third would break the lock. Thereafter they would work together to transfer the packages to their getaway fork lift truck.

What actually happened was that the rammer hit the wrong end of the van, was sprayed with gas by mistake and the third wasted precious seconds battering away at an unlocked door.

Awaiting trial they were invited for frank, round the table discussions with the police and, as sometimes happens, one broke down and told the truth but the other two lied steadily and completely.

SLUGGER Toddy rammed the van.
Ugly tried to break the lock.
TODDY Ugly sprayed the gas.
I rammed the van.
UGLY I rammed the van.
Toddy sprayed the gas.

Just for the prison record, can you say who had which job?

Fraudulent Conversion (??)

It is no surprise to those of us who receive gas bills for one million pounds and a demand for £0.00 from the rates people that computer systems can be easily corrupted.

SOLUTIONS ON PAGE 186.

Fergus, Howard and Gerald had quite a business going when one of them copied the key to the computer room, another slipped in after hours and arranged for the machine to print cheques for them and the third went to the bank to cash them.

When caught they, like so many others, thought that false admissions of guilt might hide the real state of affairs, so in the two statements made by each, one told the truth both times, another gave one honest fact and one false and the third offered two untruths:

FERGUS I copied the key.
Gerald changed the program.
GERALD Howard had the key copied.
Fergus collected the money from the bank.
HOWARD Fergus changed the program.
Gerald made the key.

Can you work out just who did what?

A coach driver's egg sandwich.

Lorry Load Of Lies (??)

The four crooks hauled in for questioning over the lorry hijack on the M4 near Newbury had learned, while picking their mothers' purses, to tell the truth as much as possible. So each of them makes two true remarks and tells one lie. They thought the net result would be confusion for the force and were surprised when three

SOLUTION ON PAGE 186.

were allowed home and the fourth invited to stay until it suited a court to throw a party in his honour.

ARTHUR I was in London that day.
I know Charlie did it.
Barry and Don are good mates, they always work together.

BARRY I didn't take the lorry, I was in Norwich.
Don didn't do it.
Arthur and Charlie are as thick as ... well, thieves.

CHARLIE I was in Southampton.
Arthur took the lorry.
Arthur lies when he says I did it.

DON I was in Liverpool the day of the hijack.
Barry? – I've never met him.
Alf didn't do it – he can't drive.

Can you work out who was arrested?

Don't Bank On It (??)

Yet another gang has tried to make a withdrawal from their local branch without having previously opened an account.

When caught because their getaway bicycles were parked on yellow lines, they made the usual vain attempts to cloud the issue by making their statements a dense mixture of truth and falsehood, although each of them did do one of the actions described. One told the truth in both statements; one lied in both of his statements and the third gave one true fact and one lie.

JOE I cut the alarm.
Limey grabbed the cash.

KLIVE I grabbed the case.
Joe guarded the staff.

LIMEY I cut the alarm.
Joe grabbed the cash.

Can you help an overworked policeman fill in his report by working out what part was taken by each man in the bank raid?

SOLUTIONS ON PAGE 186.

By bovvercraft.

Shopping Around (??)

The three young ladies being interviewed about a shoplifting spree did not exactly help their case by telling less than the whole truth to the probation officer.

Fortunately, Mrs Jones was a good enough student of teenage nature to know that the defiant one actually spoke the truth all the time and that the other two made one true statement each and one false one.

KAREN Helen passed the goods.
Jenny created a diversion.
JENNY Karen passed the goods.
Yes, I created the diversion.
HELEN I took the goods out of the shop.
Jenny passed them over.

They had hoped, poor things, for their individual guilt to be hidden and took the 'you can't prove anything' attitude. But it collapsed into tears a few minutes later when the officer told them exactly who had done which of the three jobs in their combined raid.
Can you work it out, too?

SOLUTION ON PAGE 186.

Sweet Reason (??)

That welcome return to the old days when a policeman walked his beat has been particularly useful in Middlewich where Constable Potts maintains a friendly peace over the housing estate.

He knows his charges only too well, especially the children. So when little Elaine comes sobbing out the story of her bag of sweets being taken from her hand he knows he will need to have a word with Johnny and Marcus. He knows too, that one will lie completely and the other tell the truth half the time. His only problem is who will do what today.

'Well, young gents. What have you got to say for yourselves?'

Marcus spoke up first: 'Johnny snatched the bag. I ran off with it.'

Johnny came back quickly: 'I snatched the bag. Marcus didn't run off with it.'

Potts thought for a moment or two. This was a tricky one. He looked around and then called Sheila over. She's another one who has learned to tell the truth only half the time and lie solidly the other half.

'What did you see, Sheila?' Potts asked.

'Marcus took the bag. Johnny ran off with it.'

'Ah! Thank you little lady. I now know what happened.'

Do you?

Visiting Time (???)

As the November fog closed in around Baker Street, Holmes sat in the corner of his room smoking quietly.

Eventually the long silence was broken by the sound of an approaching hansom, some muffled footsteps, a knock at the door and the arrival of a visitor.

Holmes threw the stranger a swift glance.

'I would suggest,' said the great man, 'that you recover a calmer poise before embarking on your incredible story.'

'How did you know I was agitated, Holmes?' the guest asked, 'I thought I wore the mask pretty well.'

'You have a slight limp in the left leg, indicating that

SOLUTION ON PAGE 186.

you have walked round and round in small circles for some time. There is a marked indentation on the index finger of your right hand, showing that you have been writing under pressure and it is not usual for gentlemen venturing abroad of an evening to wear a nightcap.'

'Incredible, Holmes,' Watson murmured,' I didn't notice a thing.'

'Mr Holmes, we at the Butterwick Private Clinic need your help. There has been a most dreadful crime committed and we are anxious to have a speedy apprehension of the criminal before the popular press can smear our establishment.'

'The facts, if you please.'

'We have been concerned over the health of one of our more wealthy clients, Lord Sherborne, for some time and therefore keep a constant but discreet watch on his room. His condition gave no cause for alarm this evening and several visitors came and went. The nurse on duty knew some by name, or heard given names being used and deduced the professions of some who were unknown to her.'

He handed Holmes a sheet of paper (see over).

'As you can see, they seem respectable enough but it is clear that at some time in the evening one of them administered a poison to his Lordship, for we found him dead at ten this evening.'

'We can take it, I believe,' muttered Holmes, more to himself than anyone else, 'that this dose was slipped into his evening drink by someone who was, for a short time, alone in the room. To have done it before a witness would be risking too much.'

For a short while he studied the list, then grinned in triumph as he tossed the paper to his faithful friend.

'There you are, Watson. All the evidence you need to work out who killed Lord Sherborne. Though knowing you, you'll make up one of your wretched grids to help you sort out the facts. While you are at it, identify everyone else as well, won't you, my good fellow.'

Had you been in the doctor's shoes that night, would you need the five minutes or longer to say who killed his Lordship?

Messrs Davies, Finch, Marsh, Suggett. Christian names; Andrew, Cedric, James, Peter. Wives; Alison, Clare, Marie, Sonia.

8.40pm ~ The Surgeon went in with James and Mrs Davies.

8.50pm ~ Sonia left, then Suggett, Andrew and Clare, the broker's wife, went in.

9.05pm ~ The painter and Mr. Davies and Peter left, then the director's wife went in.

9.30pm ~ James Finch left with his wife, Clare. Then Alison went in.

9.50pm ~ The painter's wife and Marie left together.

The nurse is sure that each person only made one visit. She discovered Lord Sherborne dead at 10pm.

	Davies	Finch	Marsh	Suggett	Andrew	Cedric	James	Peter	Alison	Clare	Marie	Sonia
Broker												
Director												
Painter												
Surgeon												
Andrew												
Cedric												
James												
Peter												
Alison												
Clare												
Marie												
Sonia												

SOLUTION ON PAGE 185.

Time	In	Out
8.40		X
8.50		
9.05		
9.30		
9.50	X	

Peach Surprise (???)

Holmes flagged down a passing hansom.

'The grill room of the Hotel Metropole and step on it,' he ordered, as he bundled Watson into the cab.

In the restaurant, Holmes' first glance took in the four frightened diners huddled in a corner, a constable swinging a nonchalant truncheon in front of them. At a side table a seated figure was slumped into the remains of a peach surprise. Inspecter Tew of the Yard came bustling over.

'Ah, Holmes. Glad you could make it. Nasty business.'

'Ah, Tew,' said Sherlock.

'Bless you' said Watson, automatically. A withering look shot from under Holmes' beetling brows.

'Tell me all about it, Tew.'

'Five men booked in for dinner, sat at that table there. During the sweet course one slumps forward dead. Poison, and a quick one at that. Those four,' he indicated with a nod of the head, 'won't say a word – too frightened or too guilty.'

'Nothing to go on from the staff?' asked Holmes.

'Yes, though it doesn't make much sense to me yet.

The waiter has lost his order pad but recalls some of the details of what he served and he heard some names being thrown about while he was at the table.

'1. Each man had a different main course and sweet.

'2. Carter sat between Phil and Dent, who ate the trout.

'3. Sid Woodward did not order pork or steak and sat on the right of Charles who ordered the trifle.

'4. Hunter, who did not ask for steak or duck, ordered the fresh fruit and sat on the left of Phil who asked for cheese.

'5. The man who ate the steak also had the ice cream and sat on the right of the man who ordered pork, who was not Eric or Hunter.'

Without a word, Holmes strode to the table, stared at it for a few moments, turned to the inspector and, to his astonishment, said, 'This man was killed by the person sitting on his left who slipped the poison into his dish at a moment when the others were distracted by the cabaret, probably the can-can.'

'Incredible, Holmes!' Watson cried.

'A trivial case,' Sherlock muttered. 'And within your capabilities, my good doctor. Just give the officer the details of who is whom, sat where, ate what and, in particular, the name of the murderer.'

'I would do it like a shot, Holmes,' Watson mumbled. 'But I haven't eaten since lunch and they serve an uncommonly good steak here.'

For once, Holmes must provide the answers himself. Can you match his prowess and work out just who did it?

	Bert	Charles	Eric	Phil	Sid	Duck	Game pie	Pork chop	Steak	Trout	Cheese	Fresh fruit	Ice cream	Peach surprise	Trifle
Carter															
Dent															
England															
Hunter															
Woodward															
Duck															
Game pie															
Pork chop															
Steak															
Trout															
Cheese															
Fresh fruit															
Ice cream															
Peach surprise															
Trifle															

CARTER

?

SOLUTION ON PAGES 186 TO 187.

Spear Murder (???)

Holmes' eyes wandered around the room, then alighted on the body of Lord Tayble which was resting quietly on the floor with three African spears protruding from the waistcoat.

'I think they came from that stand by the fireplace,' ventured Watson.

'Quite correct, my good doctor. And that report we have just received from young Ern, the grocery boy, settles the case as to who killed his Lordship earlier today.'

'Does it, Holmes? I don't see how.'

'Think, Watson. Upon receiving no answer to his knock, he entered the hall and deposited his box upon the hall table, being too lazy to do as he should and go round the back to the tradesman's entrance. He assures us the hall was empty . . .'

'Ah! and since we have established that at the time of the murder there was just one person in each room, aside from the victim, naturally, then . . .'

'There must have been someone in the library with Lord Tayble. And yet, doubtless through fear of incriminating someone close, if not themselves, each person has claimed to be in a room different from the one they actually occupied at the relevant time.'

'Yes, Holmes. I have constructed a sketch of the situation as they would have us see it.' (See right)

'I don't see that it helps us much, there are so many places where each could have been.'

'Not if you consider the facts in conjunction with some splendidly vague and innocent-seeming questions which I have put to some of those present. It is then a simple matter to determine just who was where. Come, Watson, consider them again:

'Tara Lotte could hear a man singing and playing the piano in the room next to hers – and there is only one instrument in the house.

'The maid said that both the doors of the room she was in were shut.

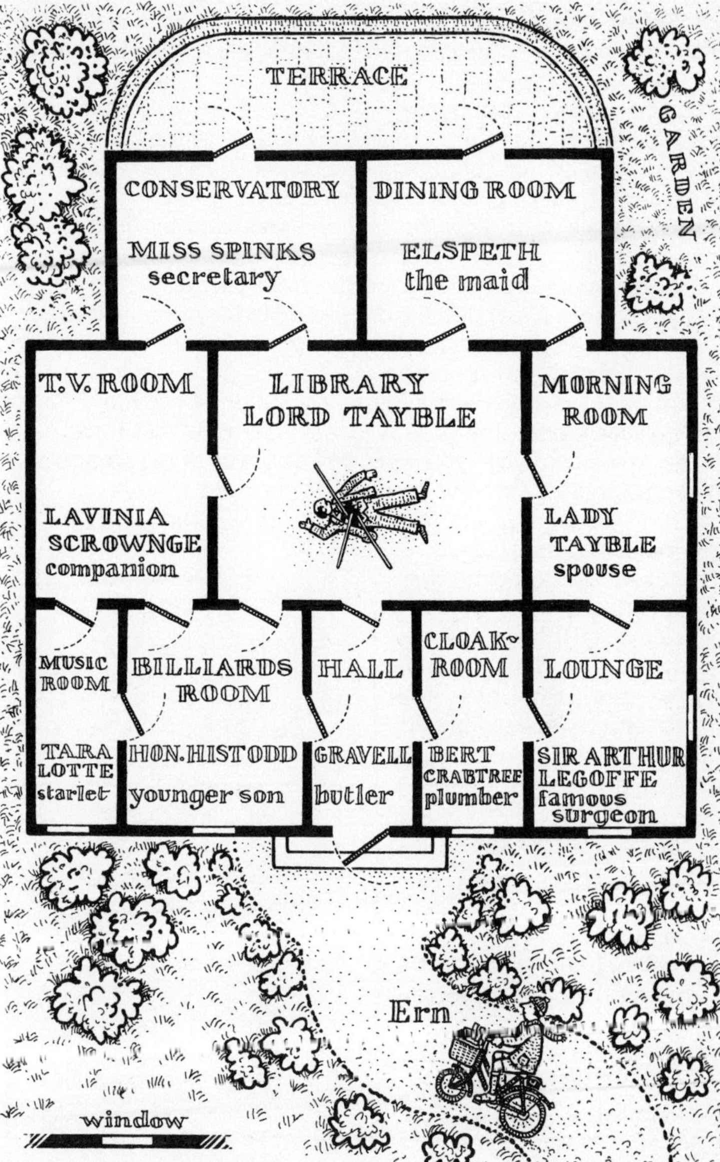
TERRACE
GARDEN
CONSERVATORY
MISS SPINKS
secretary
DINING ROOM
ELSPETH
the maid
T.V. ROOM
LAVINIA
SCROWNGE
companion
LIBRARY
LORD TAYBLE
MORNING
ROOM
LADY
TAYBLE
spouse
MUSIC
ROOM
TARA
LOTTE
starlet
BILLIARDS
ROOM
HON. HISTODD
younger son
HALL
GRAVELL
butler
CLOAK-
ROOM
BERT
CRABTREE
plumber
LOUNGE
SIR ARTHUR
LEGOFFE
famous
surgeon
Ern
window

'Crabtree, the plumber, admitted that he would have to pass through two doors to get from the room he claimed to be in to the one he really occupied.

'Lavinia states that only one of the three doors leading from the room she was in was shut – that was the door to the library. From the rustling of clothes through the two open doors she is sure that a woman was in each of those adjacent rooms.

'Lady Tayble, who says she saw and was seen by the boy Ern, occupied a room adjacent to the one she claimed to be in.

'Sir Arthur Legoffe remained in the front part of the house and Miss Spinks was aware of the Hon Histodd in the room next to hers.

'Gravell, the butler, admits to being in the billiard room helping himself to cigars.'

'And that clears the whole mystery up? I don't see how.'

'Of course it does, my good fellow. It is so trivial that I shall practise my violin while you work out who was in the library and so committed the foul deed.'

As always, the poor Doctor is left to sort out just who was where and who used his Lordship as a spear holder. **Can you give him a hand, please, and slip him the answer before Holmes breaks a string?**

	Conservatory	Dining room	TV room	Library	Morning room	Music room	Billiard room	Hall	Cloakroom	Lounge
Miss Spinks	X							X		
Elspeth the maid		X						X		
Gravell the butler								X		
Lady Tayble					X			X		
Sir Arthur Legoffe								X		X
Tara Lotte						X		X		
Hon Histodd							X	X		
Bert Crabtree								X	X	
Lavinia Scrownge			X					X		

SOLUTION ON PAGE 185.

TEAM GAMES

In this chapter you are invited to gather together a company of lively souls and pit your wits against each other as you seek the elusive answer to a baffling story. Here your clues will come from what the team thinks and what questions are asked.

Solving puzzles is, for the most part, a very solitary occupation. A railway compartment of crossword addicts looks like the annual convention of the KGB; there is no free swapping of answers and comradely chaff about missed anagrams, only eight stiff newspapers held up like fencing masks before eight grim faces, who may as well be on eight different planets.

Team Games are the complete opposite. So gather the family or friends around you, take turns to be question master, and try to fathom the strange truths behind these weird tales. For each round, one person reads the story to the rest whose task is then to explain what has happened. The reader will, of course, look up the answer. Then anyone in the group can ask a question which must be capable of being answered by a simple 'yes' or 'no'. The object is not just to find a reasonable answer to the facts given in the story but to get to the particular answer given in this book. Though the whole thing may seem impossible, improbable and impracticable, once the questions start flying, you will ferret out the solution, with tremendous fun during the hunt.

For the next round the chairperson can be whoever gave the correct solution to the last puzzle or you may prefer to give each member of your group a turn at being in charge.

Late Lamented (?)

Spare a thought for Fred and Freda,
Lying dead upon the floor.
Broken glass 'midst scattered pebbles
And a cloth half through the door.
Who were Fred and Freda?

Fur Enough (?)

A woman is walking slowly up and down at one of the larger of London's railway stations. She stops, searches her handbag and puts a coin in a slot.

She frowns, searches for another coin and is about to put that in the slot when she pauses, takes off her expensive fur coat, folds it neatly over one arm and then deposits the coin.

She grunts in disgust and quickly walks away.

What was she doing?

SOLUTIONS ON PAGE 187.

A Ferry Close Affair (?)

The man carrying the suitcase came round the corner of the warehouse at a fairly leisurely pace but immediately broke into a frantic run when he saw the ferry, fully laden, a few feet from the jetty ramp. With some considerable skill the man wheeled his arm and let go of the case at just the right instant for it to describe a beautiful arc and land with a soft thud on the car deck of the ferry. Taking a few steps back and then putting in a sprint which would have impressed Daley Thompson, the man threw himself into the air and over the water and just managed to scramble aboard the lowered end of the vessel.

The look of triumph on his face quickly turned to despair as the first mate helped him to his feet with a few words of welcome.

What did the officer say to cause such a change of mood?

The Death Call (??)

The police were quite sure; death had been due to accidental, if somewhat bizarre, circumstances.

They had been called to the telephone box by one of their associates from the river police who had noticed something odd by the bridge. Upon investigation the officers had found a man slumped in the box dying from loss of blood. Two panes of glass on either side of the box were smashed and the telephone hung from its cord.

Who was the man and how did he so tragically meet his end?

Short Stop (??)

Another true story from my days – and nights – working at a local filling station. A car pulled in one day and the driver asked for two gallons of petrol, which I served him. We then spent some time carefully searching the car before, with a sigh, he climbed back into the driving seat and moved off. As he drove away, he called out, 'I didn't really want the petrol, you know.'

Can you work out what had happened and what we were up to?

SOLUTIONS ON PAGES 188 AND 189.

Two council dustcarts.

Knees Down (??)

There they are – eleven grown men, in a straight line, crawling on hands and knees across a school playground.
What on earth are they up – or rather down – to?

Bus Stop (??)

(Another true tale – this time from the Midlands)

When the young man climbed the stairs and took his seat near the rear of the double decker waiting at Birmingham Bus Station, he saw only one other passenger – an elderly man seated near the front.

Eventually the bus left the station and headed on its way towards Worcester. Later still, the conductor came up, collected the fare from the young man and moved forward down the bus. He tapped the elderly passenger on the shoulder and, oddly, an argument quickly developed.

It ended with the bus stopping between two stops and the man being put off, still clutching his ticket.
Is there a rational explanation for the conductor's apparently harsh conduct?

The House Call (??)

When Henry Kingsbury entered the house he paused, cursing quietly in the darkness, and then fumbled his way to the lounge. He turned on the light and moved towards the fireplace where the dying embers gave only a hint of warmth. Suddenly he threw his arms upwards and leaned on the chimney breast, hands high against the wall.

He stayed like that for some seconds and then collapsed on the floor in hysterics.
Can you explain this strange conduct?

SOLUTIONS ON PAGES 187, 188 and 189.

Field Find (??)

When Vincent Dewhurst takes up a hobby, he does so thoroughly. To him, country walking means far more than a train ride from his inner city flat and a stroll round some country station's coal and livestock store. Which is why he equipped himself with thick alpine socks, stout boots, hooded anorak, field glasses and the *Readers' Digest Bedside Book of Furry Friends*.

When he returns to his concrete forest after each expedition his notebook is filled with details of all he has seen. One entry, though, puzzles him.

On the edge of Chormley Wood, close by the new housing estate, he had passed through a gate and his keen eyes had noticed several pieces of coal – and a carrot.

How they came to be there is something he cannot explain – can you?

First – And Last – Order (??)

It was unusual for the regulars of the Plucked Pheasant to hear such words but one night a stranger did enter the four ale bar and ask for a glass of water. To their further astonishment the barman reached under the bar, picked up a shotgun and pointed it at the man.

The man then thanked him and walked, smiling, into the autumn night.

Later that night the puzzled locals could not explain the events to their wives, but can you?

Little Boy Blue (??)

The policeman on traffic duty near the tower block took only a quick, automatic, mental note of the small boy who stamped angrily down the front steps and off along the road. He took a little more interest when the lad came round the block behind him and began to make a second lap of the square, still with his head down and lower lip jutting.

After three more laps the officer took advantage of a lull in the traffic to stop the boy, kneel down beside him and ask what he was doing.

What explanation did the boy give for his somewhat unusual behaviour?

SOLUTIONS ON PAGES 187 AND 189.

Domestic Tiff (??)

It is amazing how often a trivial, innocent act can set off such a row in the home that it seems only the United Nations can solve the resultant crisis. Like the wife who inadvertently puts one of her husband's socks in the top drawer and the other in the second. He, of course, always wants that very pair of leg warmers on the day he has an important meeting and is late for the train.

For Mr & Mrs Platt their version of World War Three started one night with this simple scene...

Mrs Platt is kneeling on the floor. In front of her is a long piece of wire and by her side a pile of tiny electrical components such as are used in computers. She is already very angry indeed. Her husband is also in the room, at present unaware of the bomb that is about to burst. He is speaking on the telephone.

Just why is the good lady so angry?

The Riddle Of The Crying Man (???)

Two men are lying by a hedge near a van parked by the side of a country road. One of the men is dead, the other is crying quietly with an occasional, near hysterical, half sob – half laugh. Both men are in uniform but the uniforms are not the same.

Who are the two men and how did they come to be in that situation?

Unlucky Thirteen (???)

The rush hour in Los Angeles is never an experience to enjoy. The buses, though obeying traffic regulations, always look like motorized porcupines with bits of people and packages sticking out in all directions.

On Friday 13 February, number 13, the 17.13 from the City Library made its last downtown stop before hitting the freeway and heading for the suburbs.

As usual the cry went up: 'Hey bud, shift along the bus. Twelve standing only'.

'C'mon, Mac, move it, will ya?'

What made this day different from all the rest was that, just before the doors closed an extra passenger squeezed his way aboard and the bus moved off with its fatal cargo – 13 standing passengers.

SOLUTIONS ON PAGE 187.

An argument soon developed, involving the extra passenger, the other legal standees and the man in charge of the bus. The argument became rapidly acrimonious and he stopped collecting fares and tried to persuade the gatecrasher to jump back off, while the bus was still travelling slowly. Tempers rose between the two men, a fight developed and the 13th passenger fell dead from a blow to the head.

The man was tried on a charge of murder one, found guilty and sentenced to death in the electric chair.

His appeal failed and eventually he was taken from Death Row, given the last rites and strapped into the chair. At a nod from the governor the switch was thrown. Nothing happened. The chair was checked but found to be in full working order. Again the ritual was repeated and the switch thrown. Still nothing happened.

Eventually the guilty party was taken to another prison and again taken through the awful procedure of being affixed to the chair and the switch pulled. Still nothing happened – he even managed a weak smile.

Eventually, the authorities ran out of chairs and the man was paroled, having been considered to have suffered enough for his crime.

Just what was it that saved the man?

Dash It (???)

It was a very hot summer's evening as Peter Irvin strolled along the quiet avenue in the residential estate just north of Middle Yammering. He appeared to have little on his mind when he stopped, looked first puzzled and then alarmed.

He listened intently, head to one side, his left ear a dish aerial seeking the source of some distant message. Then he was off, dashing across the road, narrowly avoiding a collision with a very large boy on a very small BMX, vaulting a garden wall and rushing up the rose-bordered path of a suburban semi.

Without hesitation he attacked the front door and burst in – to be confronted with a very surprised and irate lady who, with each passing second, was becoming as explosive as a match in a firework factory.

Can you give some rational explanation for the man's behaviour which will mollify the lady?

SOLUTIONS ON PAGES 187 AND 188.

A Moving Experience (???)

A young man is drawing. Slowly, he leans forward then stops drawing. He runs a few steps and starts drawing again.

Once more he leans forward then stops drawing and runs forward again.

He keeps doing this for a while until eventually he stands still.

What is he doing?

Down – And Out (???)

It is Saturday morning in the High Street. A man is lying down in the road between two stationary cars.

What is he doing there?

Stringing You Along (???)

(This one is also true – on my honour!)

I was working late one Sunday night at a local filling station when a car pulled in. Despite the dreadful weather the side windows were down. Inside were a very bedraggled couple. He was in the driving seat with a length of string going across his body and out of the window. His wife, in the front passenger seat, was clutching the end of the string in one hand, and, in the other, the end of another piece of string which disappeared out of her window.

Unfortunately, I was unable to help them.

What was their problem, and what had they done about it?

Ah – Agh! (???)

Two men were sitting at a table. For 2 hours and 43 minutes there had been complete silence. Quite suddenly one of the men stood up with a yell of triumph – which quickly turned into a shriek of agony.

What were the men doing – and what happened to one of them?

SOLUTIONS ON PAGES 188 AND 189.

CARDBOARD AND COUNTERS

Before television took over the sitting room and stifled all activity, mechanical puzzles and games delighted many generations of children and adults. Here is your chance to make, and play with, puzzles which are Victorian in style but new in concept. Indeed, puzzles like Reversit and Square Around have never appeared in a book before, so you have an opportunity to achieve a World's First with the best solution.
This chapter forms the basis for many evenings of pleasure and creative entertainment.

Coin Op (?)

The meter needle on this strange coin op is hovering dangerously near *empty*. To save the washing from disappearing down the waste pipe it must quickly be fed with one each of the coins from 1p to 50p. But the coins must go in the compartments in such a way that adjacent boxes must not have coins with adjacent values. In other words the 2p must not be next door (in the same row and column) to the 1p or the 5p and the 20p must not be next to the 10p or 50p and so on.

To help avert the disaster one coin, the 5p, is already in place and the 20p will be to the left of the 1p.

Hurry now! Can you find the five coins and pop them into place?

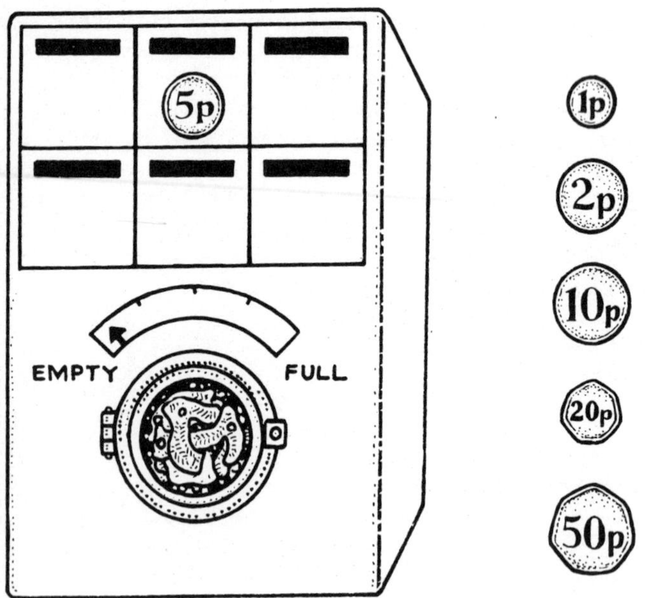

SOLUTION ON PAGE 189.

High Die Hi! (?)

All you need for this rather novel little game is a pencil and a standard die. With luck you will have a die which just about fills one of the squares on the board; if not, it might be an idea to draw a board to fit whatever die you managed to find underneath the settee!

The idea, naturally, is to roll the die in such a way that you end up with the highest score you can.

Our score of 28 is not very good so you might like to try and beat it on the board on page 133.

For fun with family and friends make up your own grid, one for each player, place each die the same way up at the start and set your digital watch to an agreed alarm time and away you go. Whoever has the highest score when the watch bleeps is the winner.

On your own at the moment? There are two more boards on page 134 for you to pit your wits against.

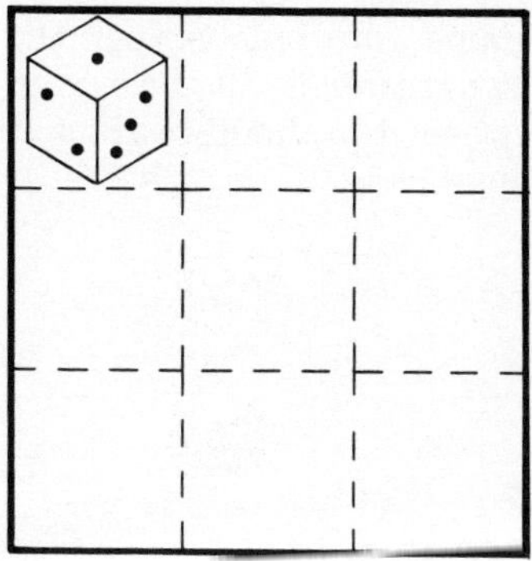

1
TO START
Place the die in the top left corner with the 1 spot on top, the 2 spot facing towards you and the 3 spot on the right.

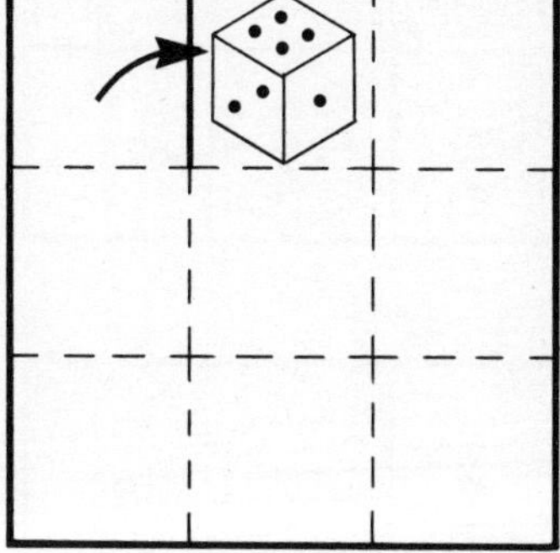

2
TO MOVE
Roll the die a quarter turn over a bottom edge so that it moves into an adjacent square. Then draw in the line the die has just rolled over.

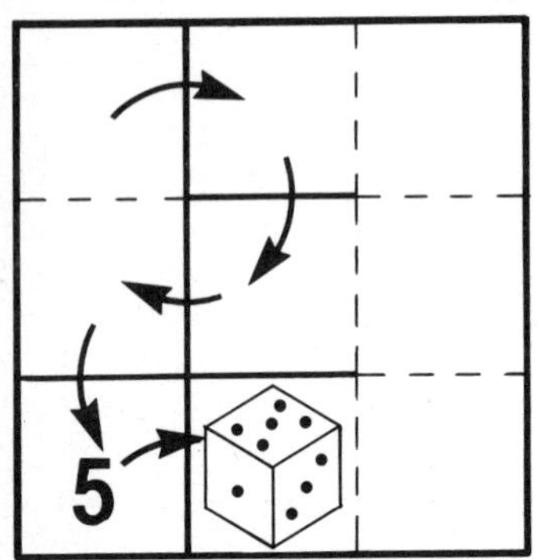

3
FILLING A BOX

After several rolls you will eventually roll and draw a line which completes a box (just as in the children's game called *Boxes*.) As a box is completed it scores points. The number is whatever is on top of the die at that move and the score is put in the box.

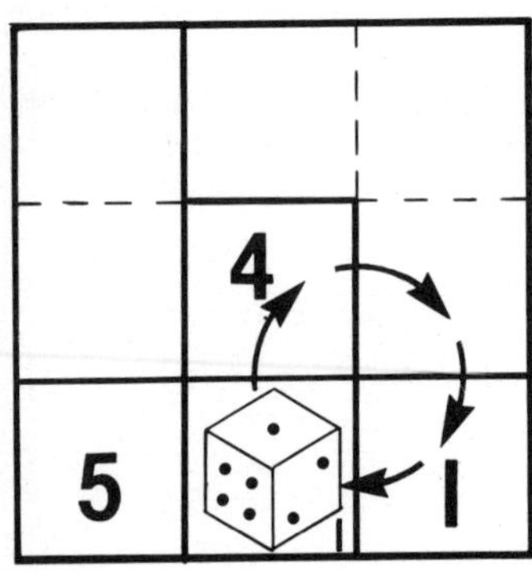

4
TWO BOXES FILLED AT THE SAME TIME

Drawing a line may complete two boxes. Put the top die number into *both* boxes. (Lift the die carefully and be sure to replace it without twisting it round.)

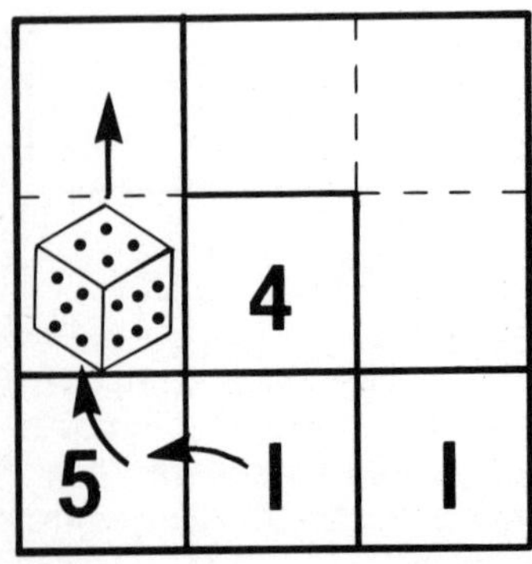

5
SPECIAL RULE

You cannot roll the die over a line which is already drawn in unless you have no other choice. Here, the die must be rolled upwards.

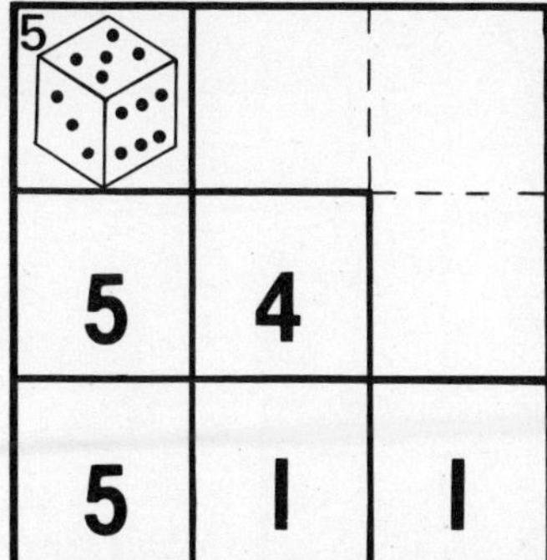

6
FREE ROLL
In this position you can roll to the right or down as both lines are already drawn.

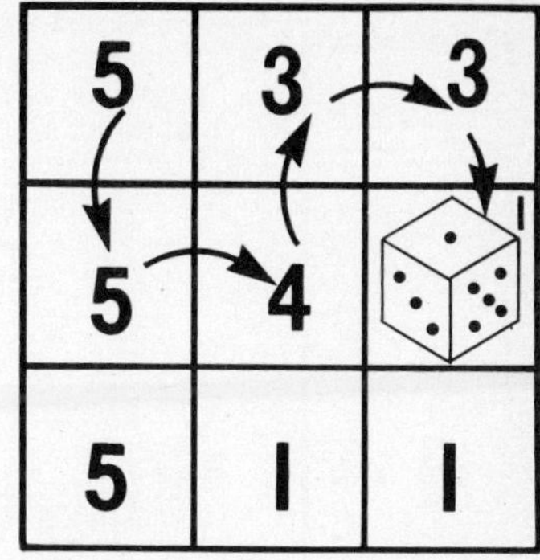

7
THE END
When all the boxes have been completed add up the numbers to get your total score. Here it is 28.

See how many points you can score on this board and the ones on the following page.

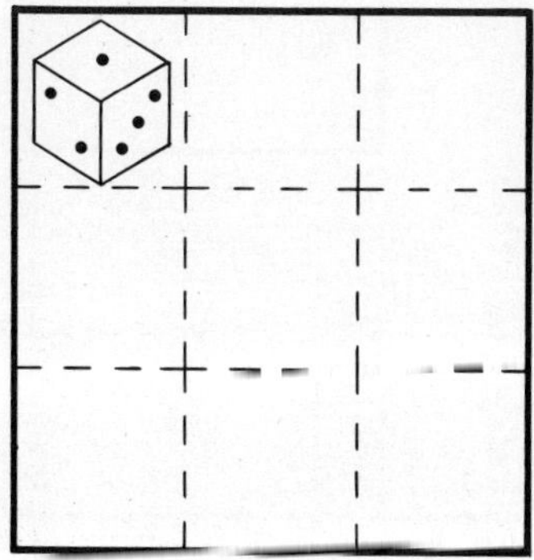

SOLUTION ON PAGE 190.

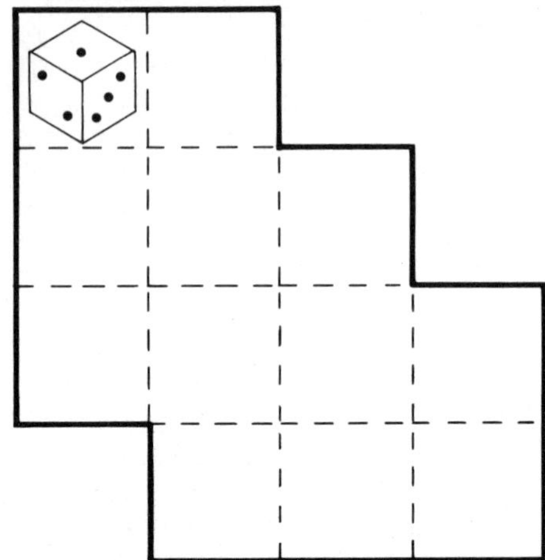

Target Score : 60 or more.

Top Score . . . ?

SOLUTION ON PAGE 190.

Over Knight Stop (?)

Never mind the Round Table at Winchester; dismiss it as nothing more than a medieval mistake. Thanks to the excavations at the bottom of his Somerset garden, Walter Wall has unearthed the original genuine table.

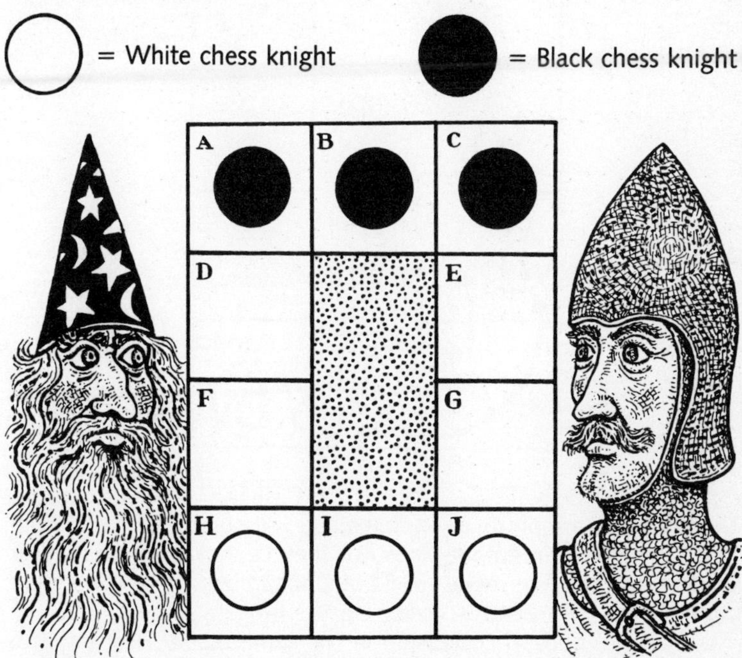

The roundness of the structure is revealed as a figment of Malory's imagination; as is the vast array of titled gents, each dressed, like a millionaire sardine, in his private tin can. In truth, the weekly meetings were lucky if all six knights turned up and Arthur sat, very carefully, to one side with Merlin opposite.

To the superstitious Arthur it was unfortunate that the black knights were on his right and the white knights on his left.

As everyone was only too well aware, it is vital to keep black knights on your left and white knights on the dexter side. Which means six knights hopping about until they are seated correctly, white at the top and black at the bottom.

Naturally they will hop like knights – two places in one direction and one at right angles as if they were playing chess.

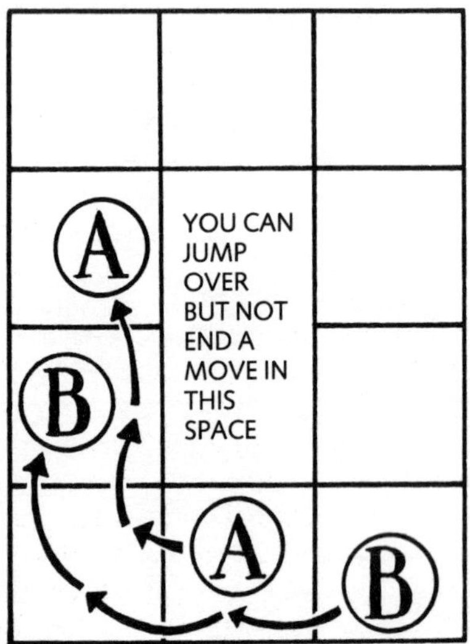

These knights are pretty agile chaps and will hop merrily over each other to land in an empty place but they cannot land on another knight – the crash of metal would be unbearable and it would take more than a tin opener to separate them again. One knight can make several hops in succession in the same move. He can jump over the space in the middle but cannot end a move there.

Merlin is already becoming impatient and is likely to break out at any moment in a rash of spells so, quick! Can you cast your own counters on the board and switch them over in the fewest number of moves?

Change In the Weather (?)

Sales at the Take-Me-Home Novelty Shoppe on Maricoombe seafront were down. True, there was a queue stretching from the front door right down to the beach, but that was for the ET Rock Arcade two doors along.

SOLUTION ON PAGE 189.

As Gus Johnson stared glumly at the piled up stock he could only blame himself for going off to the races on the one day when all the sales reps called round.

His assistant had not chosen very wisely. What demand could there be in a northern resort for a floppy hat which said 'Kiss Me Quick' in Japanese? Who was likely to buy suntan lotion in a ten gallon drum? And as for the puzzle book – was there another one in the country where the 'Spot The Difference' problem had only *one* picture?

Gus shook his head sadly, which was a mistake because it brought into view the plastic weather houses, all 200 of them. Who else but his Jim could claim there was a sure-fire winner here when the happy face said WET and the sad face DRY?

Still, there was hope for this item as the letters were written on plastic tiles set in a plastic tray and, though they could not be lifted off, they could slide around within the ten squares and so it might be possible to change the words over. (See picture on page 138.)

Gus sighed, he had tried and eventually succeeded, but converting all the stock would be a long job. If only he could find the quickest way of doing it it might at least make the task bearable.

To try to find the answer he has copied the grid, numbered the squares and made six counters from card for the letters.

His first moves are:

2 to 7; 1 to 6; 7 to 1.

Can you give him a hand by carrying on from there and finding out how to swap the words over?

To test your seaside skill here's how you can rate your effort:

Number of Moves	**Rating**
Over 45	Windy!
41 – 45	Dull with fog patches.
36 – 40	Fair.
31 – 35	Bright intervals.
26 – 30	Good – a few scattered showers.
Under 26	Excellent prospects.

SOLUTION ON PAGE 189.

1
W
2
E
3
T
4
5
7
6
8
D
9
R
10
Y

Reversit (??)

Puzzlers of the world, unite! We are an endangered species. This deplorable modern fad of keeping fit is in danger of wiping us out.

Just as we settle into a deep armchair with the feet on the mantelpiece and the mouth sucking a thoughtful pencil, in itself sufficient exercise for any right thinking person, a mass of joggers passes the window urging us, with twisted facial gestures, to get up, out and join them.

We refuse, of course. But we are left with that nagging feeling that perhaps we should go along with the tide of opinion.

It is fortunate that doctors advise beginners to stop the activity as soon as the breath becomes short which in our case means we can legally give up while still struggling into the raincoat and woolly socks.

As we collapse again into that armchair the feeling of guilt remains. If only there were some activity which looks physical enough to delude the passer-by but which is more to our intellectual taste.

Reversit is just that – a hobby puzzle so physically hard and mentally mindbending that it could serve all your needs right through to the next century.

It is also your chance to achieve a world first, no one has yet discovered the best solutions to the puzzles, though we assure you that, tough as you may find the going, all can be solved and probably in less than 60 moves.

First, the physical part. You will need nineteen reversible counters, perhaps you have the game Othello or its ancestor, Reversi. If not, you could use nineteen coins and have 'heads' and 'tails' instead of colours. In emergency, and be sure to get your doctor to check you over before attempting this, you could glue black and white draughtsmen together to make attractive double-sided counters.

If your counters are of suitable size, you could play on the board shown here, which is a miniaturized Solitaire frame; otherwise mark out your own version on card or wood, making sure the squares take whatever size counter you are using.

The basic idea is to place all the pieces white side uppermost and leave just one square empty. In these puzzles we use C3 but you can try other squares. On each turn one counter can move like a knight in chess and land in the one empty square on the board. As it lands, *it is turned over* to show the opposite colour. (See the illustrations on the following page.)

A4, D1, E4 or D5 can move into the empty square.

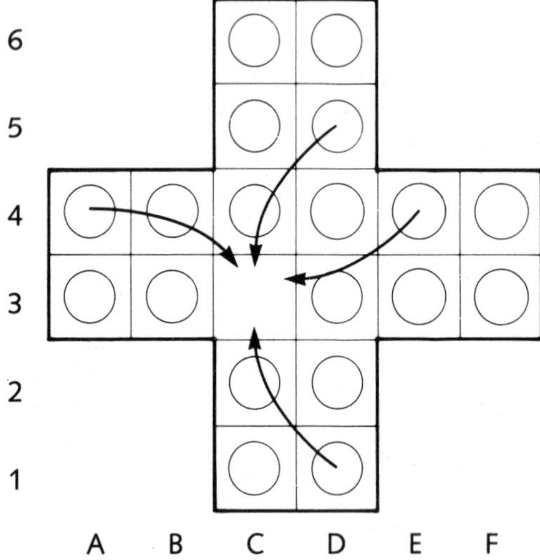

Move: D5 to C3. The counter is turned over as it is moved.

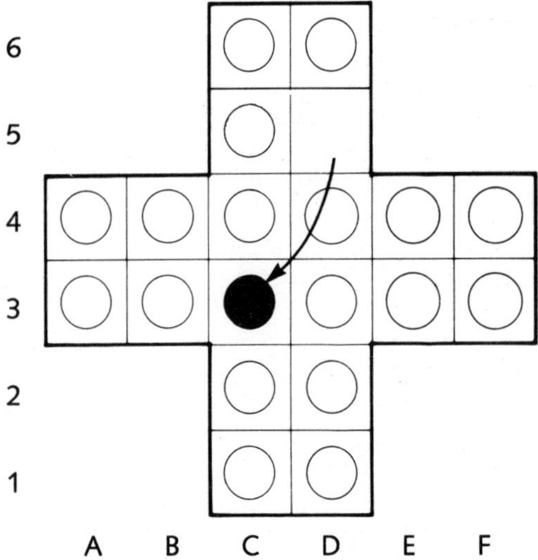

After the move you make 'captures' as in Reversi. Any counters lying in a straight line between the one which hasjust been moved and another of the same colour are turned over. The straight lines are horizontal or vertical only, not diagonal.

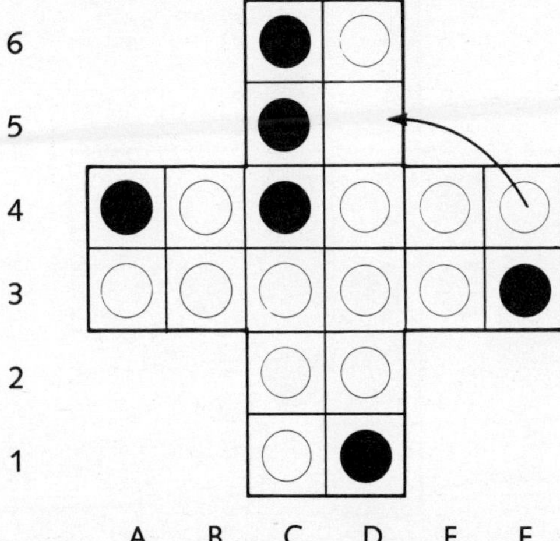

Counters at D4, D3 and D2 are trapped between the blacks at D5 and D1 and are turned over to black.

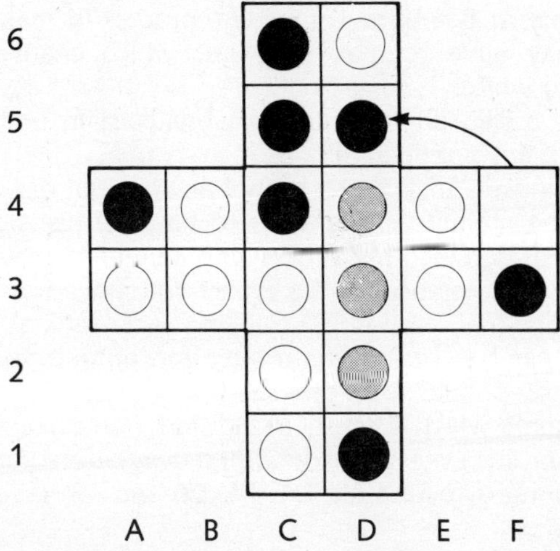

The black counter at C1 has moved to D3. The black counters at B3, C3, D2 and E3 are all captured and turned over to show white.

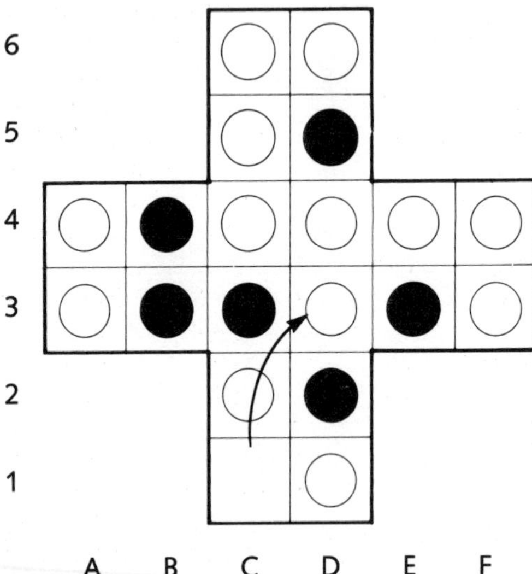

The idea is to end up with all the counters the other side up. The empty square at the end of the game does not have to be the one which was empty at the start. During the process of making the change you may have to make captures which change black counters back to white.

Give yourself a slap on the back and breakfast in bed if you manage to solve this puzzle at all!

You may feel in early trials that it cannot be done but rest assured it is possible. The ultimate challenge is to find out just how few moves you need to take; the letters and numbers around the diagram give a grid reference for the square you move from which can be written down.

More benefit can be obtained from the effort put into making it by the variety of puzzles you can set up and try. Apart from changing the square which is empty at the start, you can choose to have 0, 1, 2, 3, or 4 counters already turned over before you begin moving. The counters to turn are D1, F4, C6 and A3. (See pages 143 and144.)

Starting Positions

1

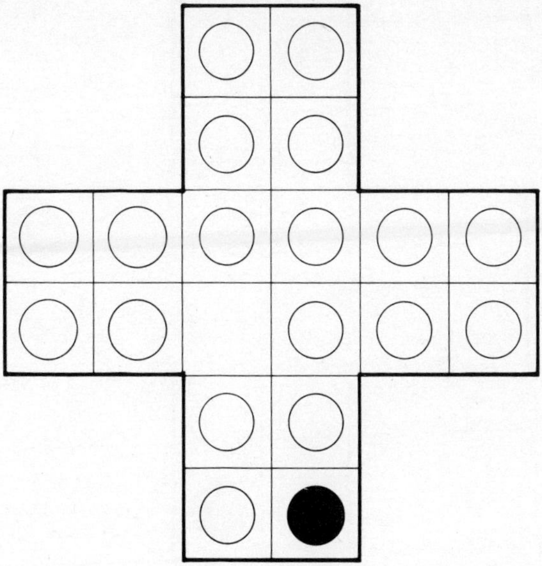

2

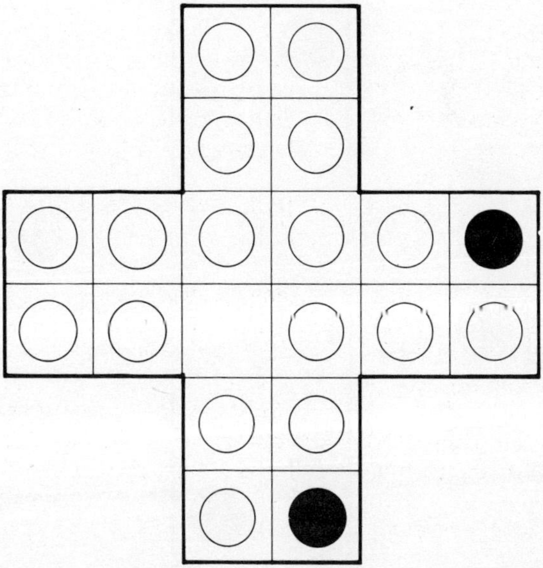

Starting Positions

3

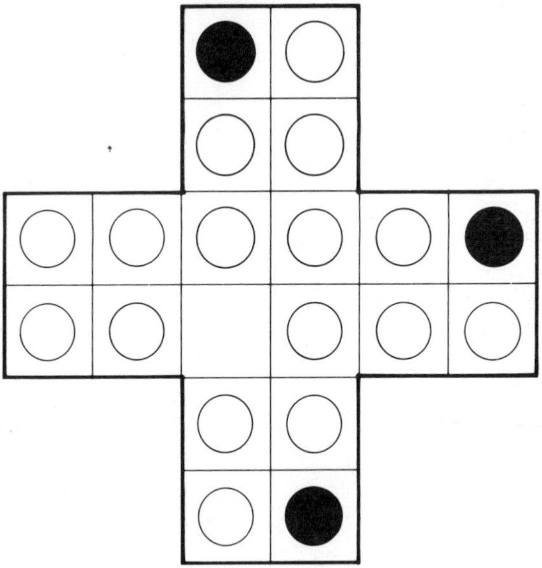

4

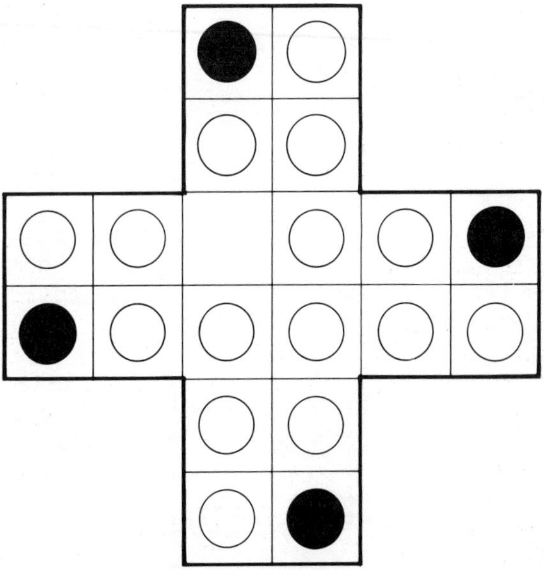

Since this is a genuine new puzzle with no past history we will not be offering any solutions here, thus giving you that real chance to climb a puzzler's Everest without leaving the comfort of your central-heatingside.

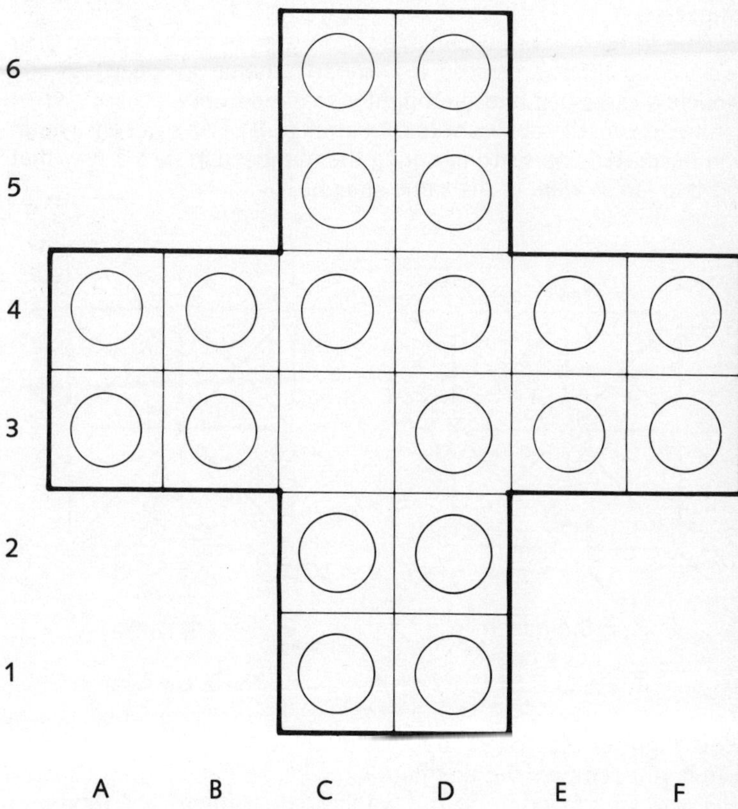

Queens High (??)

From the court of Ali Tel comes that old, old story. This Prince has 64 wives, a palace which in summer has a river at the bottom of the garden and in winter a garden at the bottom of the river, 2 very plain daughters and an eternal stream of would-be sons-in-law attracted by father's wealth rather than the beautiful nature of both princesses.

True to form, these unsuitable suitors are required to prove their worth and Ali has devised a two-part scheme to weed out the hopeless cases first and the brighter sparks second.

In part one the applicant had to arrange 8 of Ali's queens within the decorated courtyard (ignoring the numbers) in such a way that no two ladies were in the same straight line.

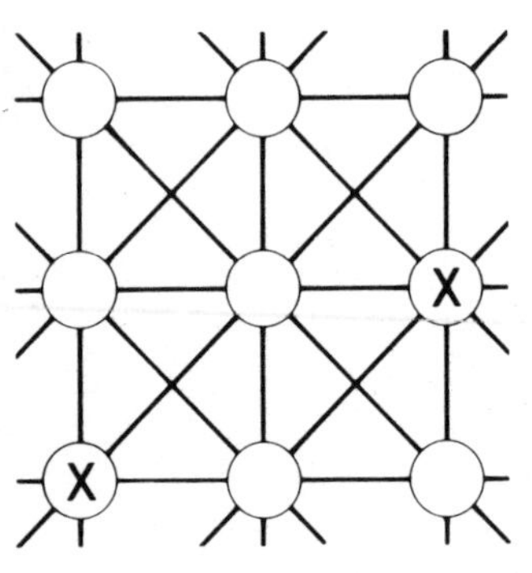

X = the queen

These are right.

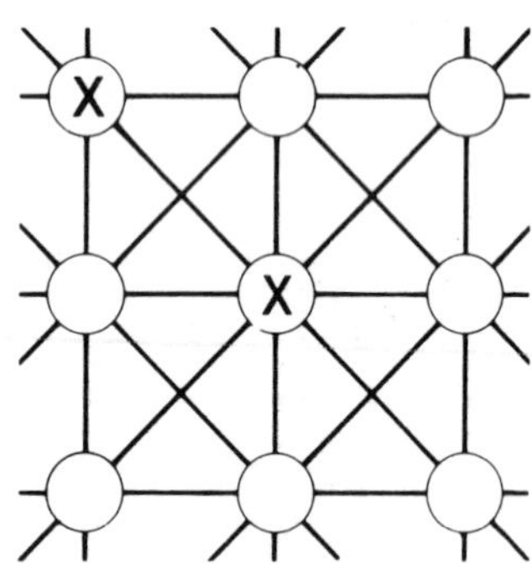

X = the queen

These are wrong.

You might like to collect together 8 counters and a chessboard to see if you can pass the first hurdle.

Those who failed to do this within the passing of one thousand grains of sand from the celestial glass to the copper pot – roughly five minutes – were required to undergo the usual early morning haircut carried out by the court barber and his curved razor.

Those left on the shortlist went on to part two – arrange those same 8 ladies as before with none in the same straight line, so that the numbers they stood on added up to the highest possible total.

Anyone who failed that test was taken to the nearest crossroads and despatched in four different directions!

Should any genius actually find the highest score then the trial was over and he won the princess's hand – what happened to the rest of her, history does not relate.

Since marriage to either princess (or both) is a better fate than any alternative, can you climb aboard your magic carpet, transport yourself to ancient Turkey, present yourself at the palace gates and win the hand of not one but both princesses?

FATIMA

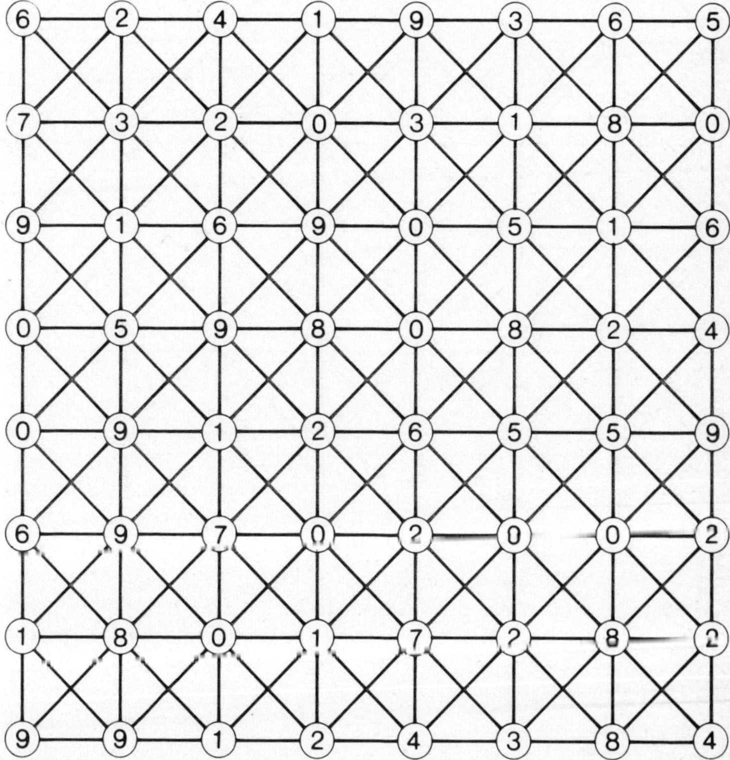

SOLUTION ON PAGE 190.

MINIMA

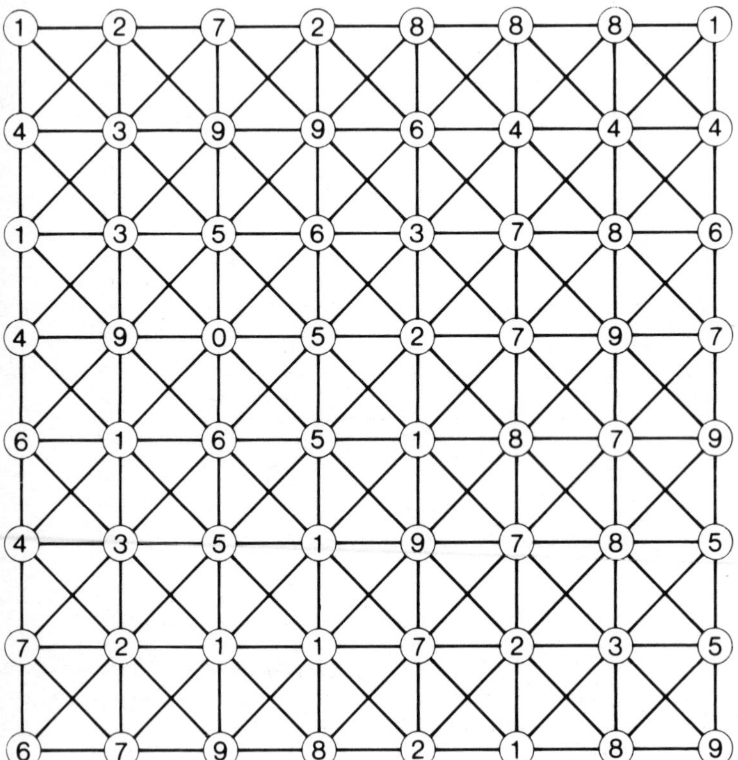

SOLUTION ON PAGE 190.

Square Around (???)

No, no need to look again. After a quick double take you have correctly realized there isn't a lot wrong with our friendly acknowledgement of your puzzling skills.

Just the L and A to switch around to make the bottom word PAL instead of PLA.

Unlike other good quality, sliding puzzles pouring out from the darkest depths of Taiwan, this one appears to be suffering from a major fault – with all nine squares occupied, how can anything slide?

Usually there is a spare square and we must admit that to have one would make things that much easier.

The best alternative on offer is to have two doors and a connecting corridor. The doors, though, are automatic.

Only one letter can pass through and occupy the corridor at any one time.

As the letter leaves the main area, the door it passes through locks so that the letter can only re-enter the grid by the other door. If you leave by one door you must enter by the other and vice versa.

Having shifted one letter into limbo, as it were, the other eight can be moved around until you, and they, are dizzy.

Then, when you wish it, make the square by the in-door empty and the letter can return.

A letter returning has the effect of unlocking the mechanism so either door can be used to move a letter out again.

As well as the problem given here you can make up your own using the same nine letter squares. Simply put them into the grid in any way you like and slide them around until they read

YOU
WIN
PAL

For any of these puzzles it is a sufficient achievement to complete the task but for those who like a stiffer challenge the main problem shown here can be solved in just 21 moves.

SOLUTION ON PAGE 189.

CALCULATOR'S CORNER

Don't panic! Only simple arithmetic is involved and no teacher will lean over you with a red pen to cross out your efforts. This chapter may even help children survive modern education.

Spot The Number (?)

This little game is a test of mental agility and can be played anywhere there is room to roll four dice by any number of players, young and old.

First of all, one player selects a target number, which should suit the age of the players and should probably not be more than about 300.

The four dice are rolled by another player and retrieved from under the carpet, the dog's left ear, Dad's beerglass or wherever else they have landed.

The four top numbers are noted and then used by the players, working against each other and a clock if you wish, to get as close to the target number as they can.

The rules are quite simple:

1) All four numbers must be used, once each.
2) The numbers may be added, subtracted, multiplied or divided.
3) The numbers may be combined together in pairs or even threes to form two and three-digit numbers.
4) A player who scores the target number gains three points. A player who forms a number which is within five of the target scores one point. (You may prefer to score highest points to the player nearest to the target, down to lowest points for the player furthest away – with, perhaps, a bonus for anyone actually making the target number exactly.)

Thus with a roll of 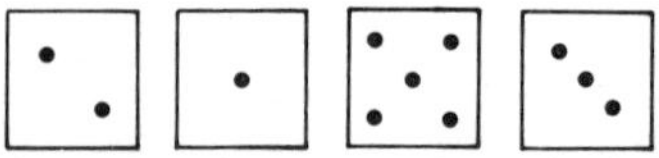 it is possible to achieve a target number of 32 by using the 5 and the 3 to make 53, the 2 and the 1 make 21 and 53 − 21 = 32.

If the target was 96, then it can be scored by joining the 5 and 1 to make 51; 51 − 3 = 48 and 48 × 2 = 96.

A game can be as many rounds as there are players, so each has a turn rolling the dice, or an agreed number of rounds.

In our little competition your aim is to score 30 points in the 10 rounds. Can you do it?

	DIE ROLL				TARGET
A	1	3	4	6	32
B	2	2	5	3	20
C	1	4	4	6	1
D	2	5	3	6	33
E	3	4	2	5	13
F	2	3	3	3	32
G	5	5	5	6	605
H	2	4	5	5	277
I	1	3	6	2	29
J	6	6	6	6	111

SOLUTION ON PAGES 190 to 191.

Sum Score (?)

If we were to ask you to use three 3's to make 3, then there would be no problem, would there?

Instead we will ask you to make a variety of digital delights using the same digits.

To combine the digits you are allowed to use $+$, $-$, $\times$, and $\div$ and you may throw brackets around to make things clear.

The aim is not just to achieve the number but to use the simplest methods, so rate your efforts as follows:

If you use $\div$ anywhere score just 1 point for that answer.
If you use $\times$ anywhere, score 3 points.
If you use only $+$, $-$, then score top marks of 5 points.

So if you were to make 3 from three 3's by the sum $3 \times 3 \div 3$ you would gain just one point. But if you came up with $3 + 3 - 3$ that would be worth five points. You can, of course, put the digits together to make numbers, such as 555.

On your marks, then off for a quick sprint through these five posers.

A. Use four 4's to make 44.
B. Use five 5's to make 55.
C. Use six 6's to make 66.
D. Use seven 7's to make 77.
E. Use eight 8's to make 88.

Cash, Bang, Wallet (?)

When incredibly rich business man, Augustus Monge, threw a firework party last November he spared no expense in ordering a personal stock of fireworks which would let the world know just what a price he was paying for this spectacular entertainment.

As each firework reached for the sky it exploded in a shower of stars which showed coin values large enough to be seen a mile or more away. Augustus' idea was that as each gem went off his friends could work out the price as they enjoyed its display.

Which made it all the more of a pity when his deputy-under-gardener, 'Erbert by name, acting as fire-raiser and reluctant at the enforced overtime, let off three fireworks at once.

SOLUTION ON PAGE 192.

As they shot upwards the cascading stars became so intermingled that it could not be seen just how much each had cost.

Still Augustus just had time before all went black to sack 'Erbert and tell his gathering that each firework had produced five stars; that the three were of three different prices, though the prices were equally spaced out and had cost a total of £1.50.

The cheapest had cost 43p; the Silver Drops had more 2p stars than did the Cascade and the Etna did not produce any 2p stars at all.

The company looked at each other and wrinkled their brows. It was beyond them, but it shouldn't be beyond you to work out which coins made up each starburst and the cost of each firework.

SOLUTION ON PAGE 191.

Magic Switch (?)

12	13	14	15
8	9	10	11
4	5	6	7
0	1	2	3

Magic squares, as we all know, have rows, columns and diagonals which add up to the same total. Which is a state our square completely fails to achieve.

Still, you can turn it into a genuine magic square by switching two of the numbers over.

Then doing that again. And again. Once more. Yes, making just four switches of pairs of numbers will do the trick!

When you have done it all the straight lines of four numbers will add up to 30.

	9		
		6	
0			

We have even placed three of the numbers for you. Can you place the rest?

SOLUTION ON PAGE 191.

Jolly Good Show (?)

At the Much Muddling Comprehensive School the maths teacher, Mr Jolly (known to his class as 'Freezer'), believes in making 'tables' practice as interesting as possible.

Instead of weekly tests he gives his class Tables Squares where most of the numbers are missing and just enough put in to enable the children to work out what goes where.

Since the weekly chore is followed by Games the children want to get the job done as quickly as possible. They have worked out that the quicker they can find the numbers which go around the edge, the faster they can fill in the middle.

How long do you need to complete each table?

EXAMPLE: ADDITION

4 + 3 = 7

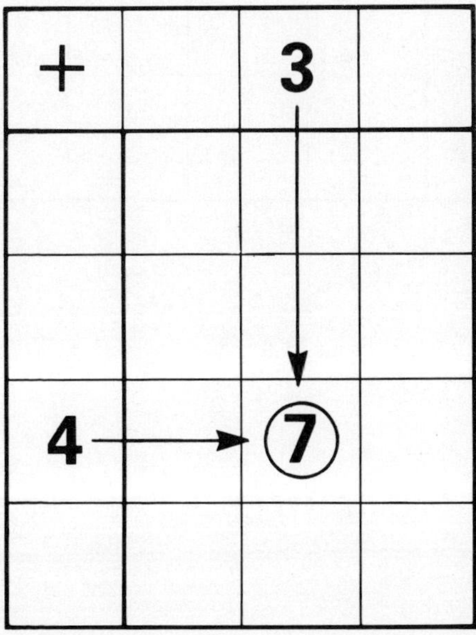

EXAMPLE: MULTIPLICATION

$4 \times ? = 12$

$4 \times 3 = 12$

×			③	
4			12	

ADDITION

Numbers to put round the edge: 0 to 9.

+	8	5			
			7	16	
4					
1					3
		11			
	11			12	

SOLUTION ON PAGE 192.

ADDITION

Numbers to put round the edge: 0 to 9.

+					
				13	
		1			2
			15		
		7		15	
			12		

SOLUTION ON PAGE 192.

MULTIPLICATION

Numbers to put round the edge: 0 to 9.

×					
	35	42			21
			18		
	5			8	
			8		

SOLUTION ON PAGE 192.

MULTIPLICATION

Numbers to place round the edge:
1 to 9 across the top.
1 to 9 down the side.

×									
				28					35
						2			
		12							
								30	
			16						
	8								
			6						
								36	
					81				

SOLUTION ON PAGE 192.

Sum Total (?)

Can you just pop the digits 1 to 9 into the square so that each line has the total given at the end of it?

To give you a start, three numbers are already in position.

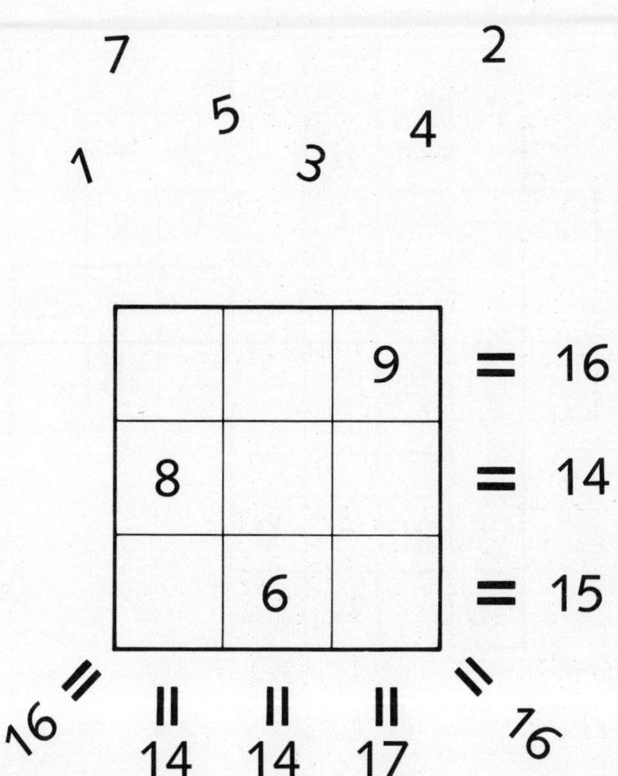

SOLUTION ON PAGE 192.

Sum Trouble (?)

In this rather weird grid, four sums going across the page have been mixed up with another four going down the page. From those which are already in position, can you work out where the rest of the figures and signs must be placed to make everything correct?

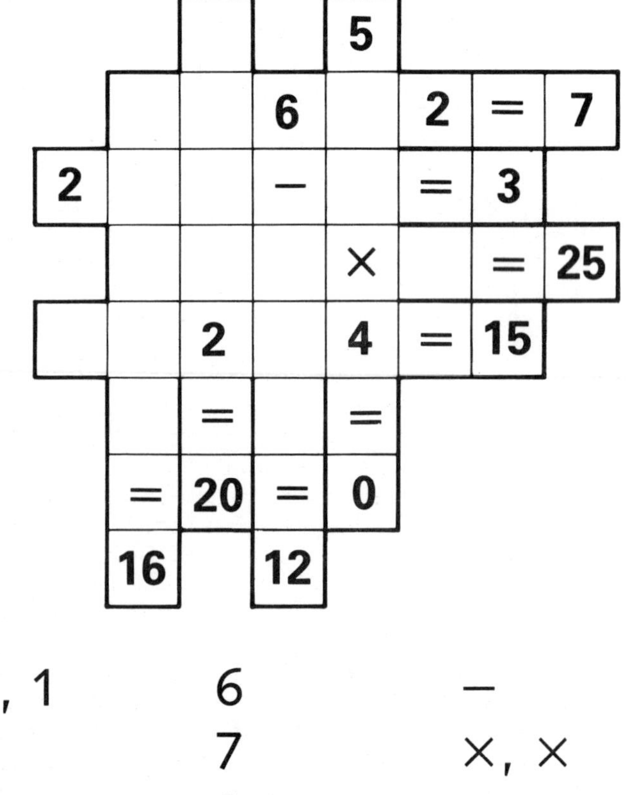

1, 1	6	−
3	7	×, ×
4	9	
5, 5, 5	+, +, +	

SOLUTION ON PAGE 191.

Fare, Please (??)

There never are more than 50 passengers on the one vehicle run by the Ben Nevis Bus Kompany but it was extraordinary when they all paid the same fare one day and offered exactly the same seven coins each, which made up the correct amount.

At the only stopping point, the driver noted that the total given by his machine was £9.79 and a quick riffle through the bag showed there wasn't a single 20p coin which he could swap for his own two 10ps for use on the café's chocolate machine.

So how many 2p coins were there in the bag?

Share Robbery (??)

You've heard of 'honour among thieves'? Forget it, at least as far as the Black Head Gang are concerned.

On their latest imitation of Robin Hood, robbing the rich in the shape of the bullion van to give to the poor, themselves, they actually got away with a number of gold bars and escaped across country until they found a deserted barn.

They set their loot in a pile and formed an uneasy ring around it, each, as their eyes closed, determined not to go to sleep.

As their snores forced the mice to put their paws over their ears one of the gang, Alf, crept forward and put half the gold bars into a bag. As an insurance, in case he was later caught, he hid one of the remaining bars in the straw and made his getaway.

Not long afterwards Clogger stirred, blinked, looked around and then made his way to the pile, which didn't seem as big as he vaguely remembered it, took two thirds of the gold bars and put them in his bag, He, too, took one bar from the remainder and hid it in the straw, just in case, and, without bothering to say goodbye, left the barn.

Ferdie was asleep for another hour before he, too, had a notion to look at what now seemed a surprisingly small haul. With a shrug he loaded three quarters of the stack about his person, hid one of the remainder in the straw as a precaution and set off towards London.

Jimmy woke up and stared in some perplexity at the single gold bar which lay in front of him and, philosophically, put it in his pocket and went out, only to be arrested at the nearby farm when he tried to buy a pint of milk with it.

How many bars did the gang steal in their Little Van Robbery?

SOLUTIONS ON PAGES 191 AND 192.

Digital Splits (??)

1 2 3 4 5 6 7

There are quite a few ways to arrange these digits into a three-digit number and a four-digit number; 123 and 4567 being the most obvious.

What we are looking for is that the three-digit number must be a multiple of 4 and the four-digit number a multiple of 3.

(Remember multiples? 12 is a multiple of 3 because 3 divides exactly into it.)

Your efforts in this direction will score points, equal to your two numbers added together.

For example, 5421 is a multiple of 3 and that leaves 736 as a multiple of 4 so the score is 5421 + 736 which is 6157.

How would you pop the digits into these boxes to make the score the highest possible?

A.

3-digit multiple of 4

4-digit multiple of 3

Now try these: again, how high a total can you manage? (By the way, double value in all these problems as you can go on to find the lowest total in each case – no extra charge either.)

B. 2 3 4 5 6 7 8

3-digit multiple of 4

4-digit multiple of 5

C. 7 6 5 4 3 2 1 0

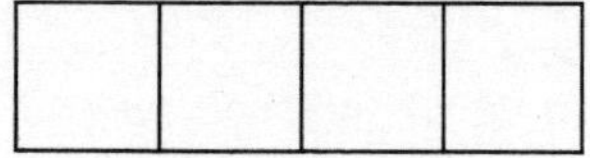

4-digit multiple of 5

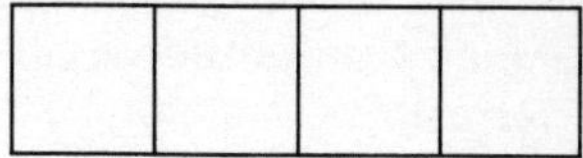

4-digit multiple of 6

D. 1 2 3 4 5 6 7 8 9

3-digit multiple of 3

3-digit multiple of 4

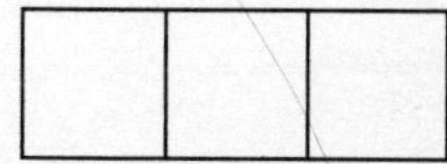

3-digit multiple of 5

E. 9 8 7 6 5 4 3 2

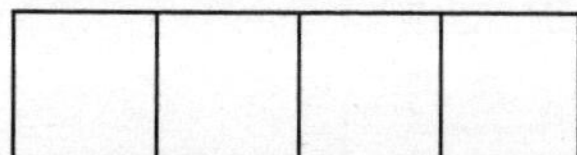

4-digit multiple of 8

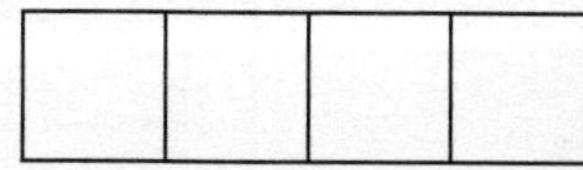

4-digit multiple of 9

SOLUTIONS ON PAGE 191.

Top Display (??)

Let the sad tale of Xavier Quidds serve as a lesson to us all.

In a lifetime spent watching what he spends and always going for the bargain, usually offered to him on a backstreet corner from the depths of a seedy-looking overcoat, he has amassed the biggest pile of junk seen outside a city tip this century.

Like this calculator, which does light up when switched on and will, if you are very careful, perform a sum or two.

Xavier has learned the hard way (he bought a gross of these!) that to avoid disaster when a key has been pressed, the next key hit must not be in the same row or column. If it is, the calculator shoots all its buttons at the user's face and expires with an electronic whine.

For instance, if you hit the 8 button you could not then hit 7, 9, or X, nor could you hit 5, 2 or +.

In any case, after hitting a number key you must then hit an operation key, then a number again, an operation key and so on.

If you are allowed to press only ten keys and a different one each time, what is the largest number you can make appear on the crystal display?

(PS: the last key you hit must be the = sign, or the number won't come up on the display at all!)

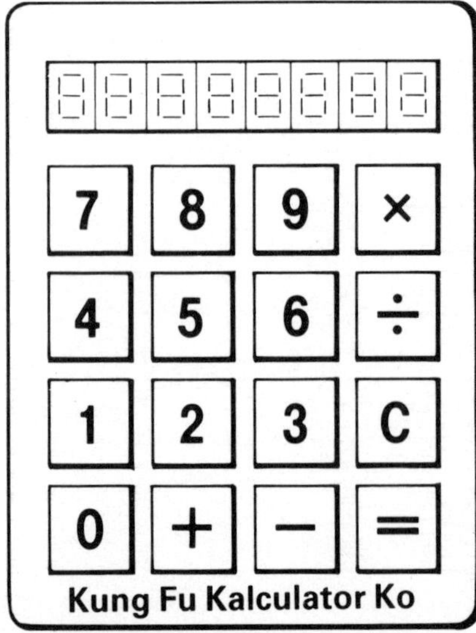

SOLUTION ON PAGE 192.

SOLUTIONS

To make sure you don't 'accidentally' see the next answer, the solutions within each chapter have been muddled up.

ODD ONE OUT

2

FIFTY-FOUR. The others are all 'square' numbers' 1 × 1; 3 × 3; 5 × 5; 6 × 6; 9 × 9.

9

7011. In each of the other numbers the digits add up to eight.

1

D. This is a left hand and all the rest are of a right hand or foot.

8

SCREAM. Each of the others has three vowels and three consonants.

15

MICHAEL. The others are forenames of recent British Prime Ministers; James Callaghan; Edward Heath; Harold Macmillan; Anthony Eden and Sir Alec Douglas-Home.

4

ORANGE. If you have all the others and a large flat table you can enjoy a game of snooker.

20

CUBE C. C contradicts E so one of those is wrong and thus the others are all correct. E agrees with F so C is the odd one out.

3

D. GOOSE. The rest are birds of prey but you are not in any real danger of being eaten by a goose – rather the other way round!

10

1749. In all the others the number formed by the first two figures divides exactly into the number formed by the last two. Thus in 1976 – 19 goes into 76 four times.

16

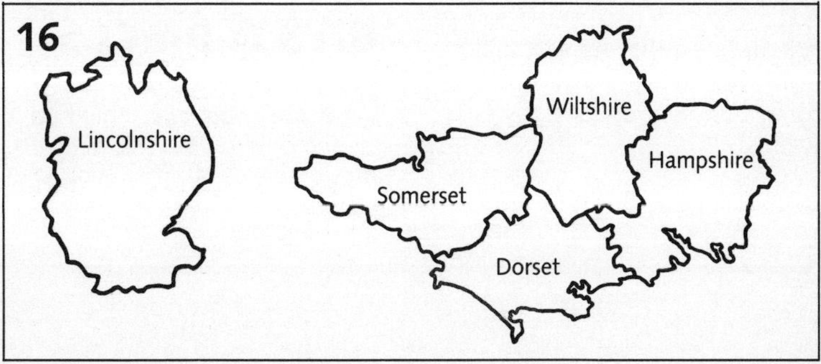

5

VENUS. Score ten bonus marks for all the reasons which make Venus such an odd planet. Here, the main reason is that all the other planets in this list have moons. But you may know that on all the planets except Venus the year is longer than the day. On Venus each day (one spin on its axis) is actually longer than one year (time taken to make one orbit of the Sun).

11

LIBRA. The sign of this astrological item is an object – a pair of scales. The other signs are of creatures. Pisces = fish. Cancer = crab. Taurus = bull. Capricorn = goat and Scorpio = scorpion.

17

B does not quite belong. The others are all rotations of each other but B is a reflection of the basic pattern.

13

D is an Alsatian. The other dogs all begin with B: Boxer, Bloodhound, Bull Terrier, Basset Hound.

18

D is from another cube. A and D contradict so the other four are correct. D contradicts B so D is wrong.

12

E is somewhat different. For all the others the squares are always on *opposite* sides of the same arm and the circles are on the same side. On E this is reversed.

7

MONSOON is a season and a rainy one to boot; the others will give you the wind up.

19

R. The rest are the position letters of girls in a netball team; WA = Wing Attack and so on. (No, boys, don't complain – you really ought to know. After all you probably bore your girlfriend silly with talk of sweepers, midfield and front runners!)

6

WEST. All the rest are seas: Black Sea; North Sea; Red Sea; Dead Sea.

14

SALE. The others are official abbreviations of American states; ALASka, MASSachusetts and so on.

BITS & PIECES

HALF-CAKED IDEA

What the good lady should do is let one child cut the cake and give the other child first choice of pieces!

STRAWBERRY SHARES

11

1

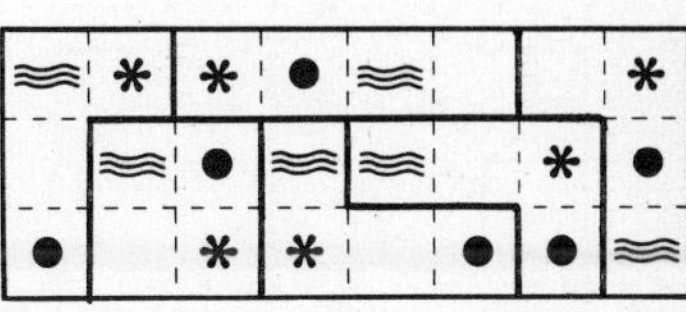

7

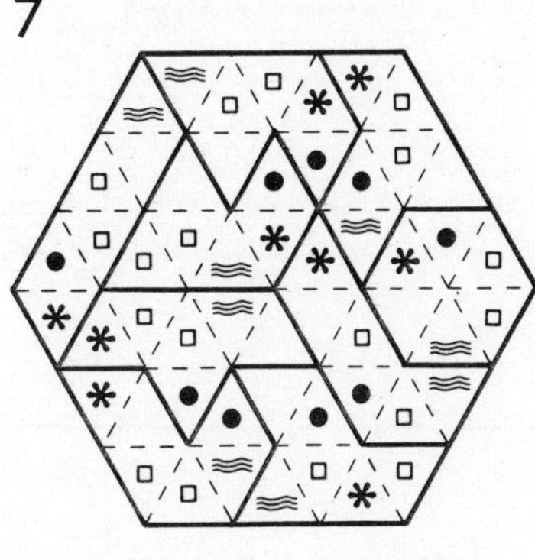

10

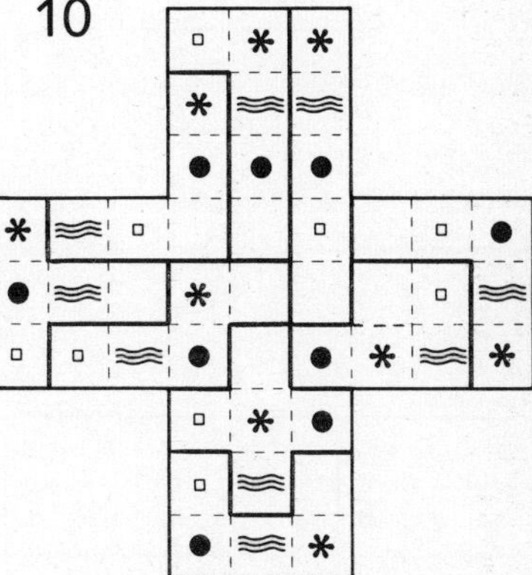

4

3

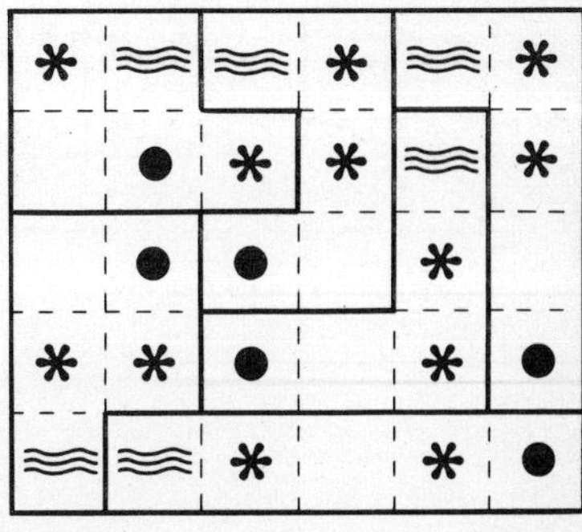

9

6

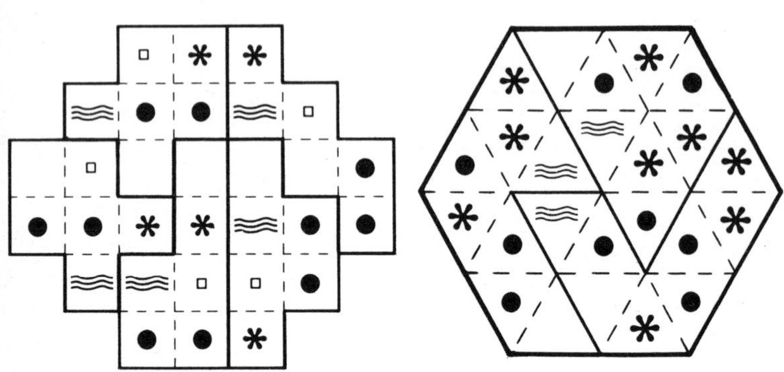

12

2

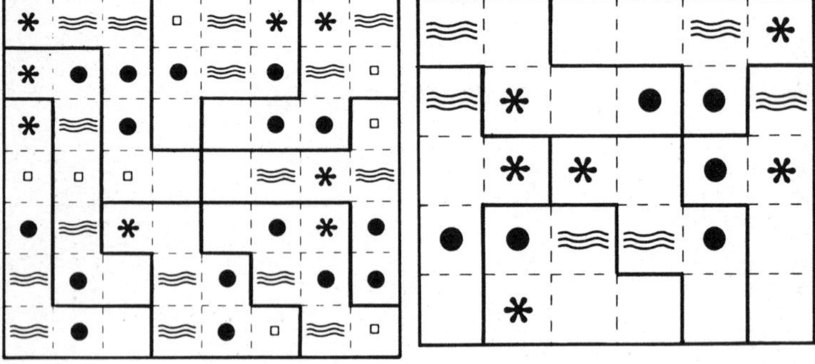

5

8

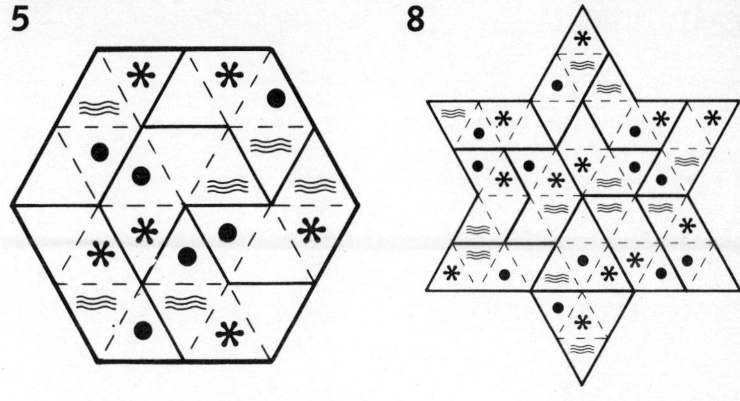

SPOT THE DIFFERENCE

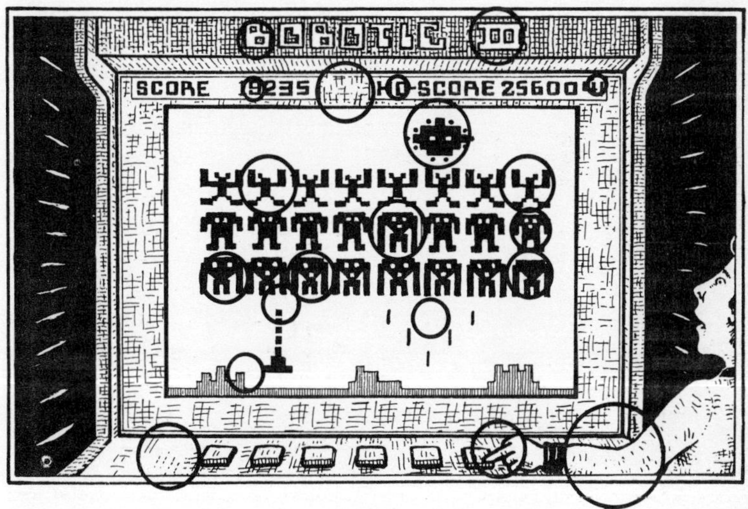

PARTY PIECES
B, D, E, A, C.

WINNING CUT
Cheryl, with that one swift flash of the knife, cut the board in half from left to right, turned her half round which meant her King could take all of her father's pieces in one move.

IN SEQUENCE
D, E, A, C, B.

CUBE BITS
Yes, it can be made.

RIDDLES
WHAT'S MY BLANK?

3 **SUGAR**
Season
Ugly
Gas
Apple
Rag

2 **POTATO**
Panel
Option
Toffee
Arch
Toe
Orange

1 **LION**
Left
Island
Offer (Occasion)
Navy

6 **HANDKERCHIEF**
Heart
Anvil
Nights
Dish
Killer
Extra
Road
Coast
Hole
Inch
Easter
Fingers

8 **MERINGUE**
Moon
Engine
Ring
Invaders
Note
Goal
Under
Ear

4 **CANDY FLOSS**
Clif**F**
Apri**L**
NO
Dres**S**
Year**S**

7 **PINE TREE**
Pin**T**
Inne**R**
Nettl**E**
Ey**E**

5 **CHIP SHOP**
Clas**S**
Hig**H**
Int**O**
Pum**P**

FILM FUN
The Umpire Strikes Back.
Return Of The Jetty.
20,000 Leeks Under The Sea.
Merry Poppings.
From Russia With Glove and Coldfinger.

WHAT'S YOURS?
Bed. (Flower bed, bed you sleep in, and river or sea bed.)

GET THIS
A golf course.

THE PLACE TO BE
Address.

BLEEP, BLEEP
A space set alight (space satellite!).

ONE, TWO, THREE...
Ewe.

SPOT THIS ONE
A die. It has the numbers 1 to 6 in spots, the total is 21.

WHAT IS IT?
The Earth.

A WORD FROM THE BARD
Water.

ACROSS THE GREAT DIVIDE
Just after she had suffered a fatal heart attack, Edwina's body was transported on a plane and crossed the International Date Line! Upon which Monday changed back to Sunday.

GARDENERS' QUESTION TIME
Carrot. Car, arr, rot.

A FIR QUESTION
Superman, otherwise Clark Kent.

CODEWORD

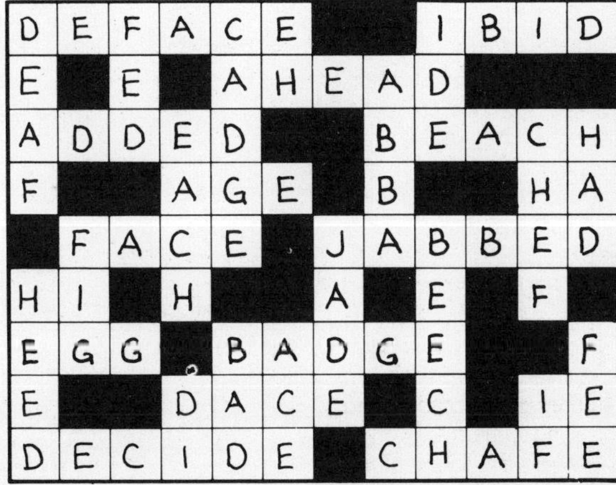

CALLING ALL PUZZLERS
Let your brain take the strain.

JUNGLE JESTER
Monkey.

HEADLESS RHYME
There was a young man from Dee
Who went for a swim in the sea.
A shark saw his flippers
And said 'whoopee kippers!'
Then ate the young man for his tea.

CRASHWORD
Washing machine.

CODESQUARE

START
TENOR
ANGLE
ROLES
TRESS

THE STORY SO FAR
Tracey Scott and her friends, Christopher and Sandra Edwards, carefully turned the key to the warehouse door. Slowly it began to open, groaning and growling like a bear disturbed during its winter sleep.

Inside the darkness crowded around our scared heroes; scampering noises set their teeth chattering in fright. Somewhere in this vast building the crooks had stashed the gold bullion.

As they groped their way along a musty, smelly wall, a switch clicked on and a brilliant shaft of light played on them.

They were trapped!

WHO DID WHAT?

THE SEASIDE SAGA

Sarah	funfair	mother
Brian	ice cream	grandad
Tim	pier	aunt
Joan	donkey ride	uncle

ROAD UP

house	name
A	Sangster
B	Dennett
C	Thomas
D	Hughes
E	Ready
F	Adams
G	Briscoe
H	Flower

MINOR LEAGUE

Bill	Bears	1
Fred	Giants	2
Leslie	Allstars	3
Tony	Bluesox	4

FLASH CRASH

The winner was Phil Davies in the Zoom. The rest of the details are:

Clive	Morelli	Streak	No fuel
John	Chappell	Lightning	Fire
Max	Bennett	Flash	Oil patch
Steve	Quest	Jet	Lost bend

FRUIT & VEG

The carrots should be in the middle row in the third box from the left. The entire display should be laid out as follows:

plums	lettuce	apples	sprouts
cabbage	oranges	carrots	pears
peaches	cucumber	grapes	potatoes

DAYLIGHT ROBBERY

Mr Lomond	Van	High Street	Knoyle View
Miss Hammett	Sports	West Way	High Street
Mrs Green	Estate	Long Lane	West Way
Mr Wilkins	Saloon	Bradley Road	Long Lane
Miss Lever	Mini	Knoyle View	Bradley Road

Miss Hammett in the sports car and Mr Lomond in the van may, to use a marvellous understatement, be able to assist the police with their enquiries.

RING O ROSE'S

Reading clockwise around the ring, the children are; Rose, Andrew, Tanya, Edward, Sarah, Colin.

TAKE IT FROM HERE

Alice	Hooper	chow mein	34
Bill	Jackson	chop suey	45
Charles	Goldsmith	special	16
Dora	Innis	foo young	21
Eileen	Farley	prawn rice	52

AMAZING MAZES

CLUED BRICK CUBE

DEVINE INTERVENTION

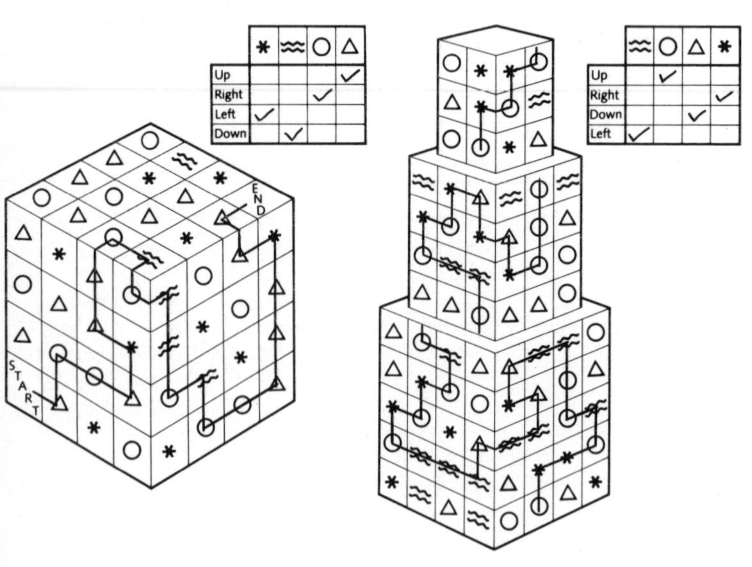

RED RIDING ROUTE

The shortest path is shown here. If you left the shops by going left, up, right, then your path is a bit longer and the wolf will be at Grannie's door!

HOME 1	1	5	4	3	3	1	6
0	1	0	1	2	2	3	4
3	5	4	1	SHOPS 1	2	0	4
0	1	1	0	4	2	1	1
2	WOODS 1	5	2	0	3	3	3
0	0	2	1	3	4	3	6
2	3	2	2	4	1	0	GRANNIE'S

THE MARSH OF MYNOG

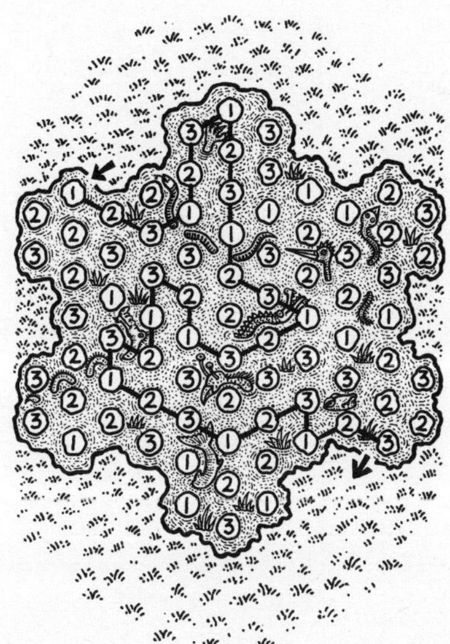

DRUNKEN ANT

Including the end, the alcoholic ant travelled through 45 squares on his journey. (And this must be his actual path.)

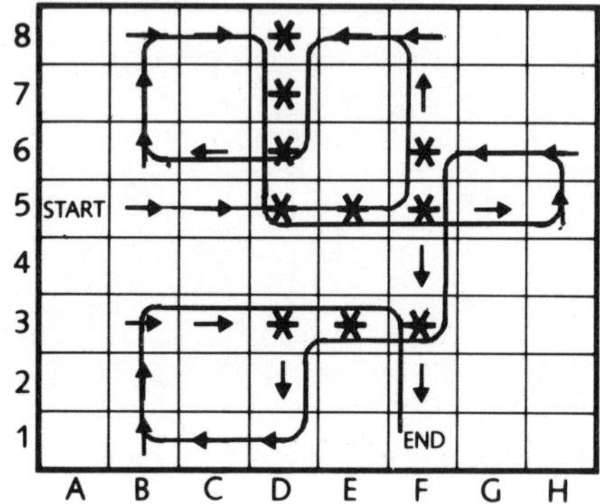

58 squares. (Again the genuine route.)

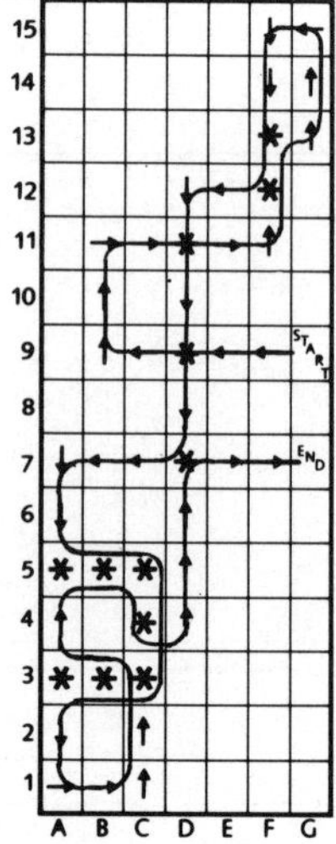

75 moves in this one but your beginning may not be the same as this sample.

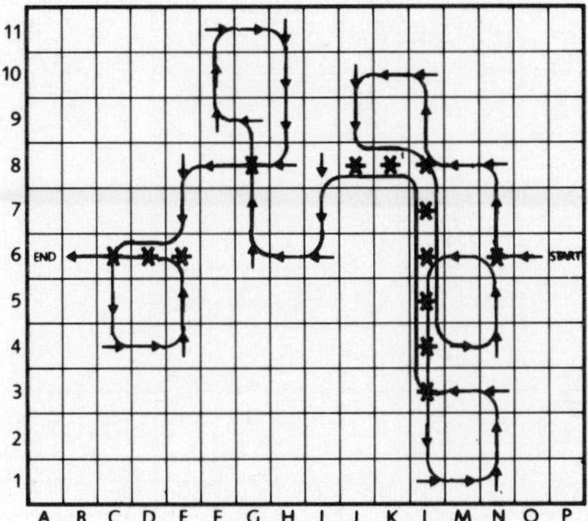

This shows one of several possible routes which take 124 squares.

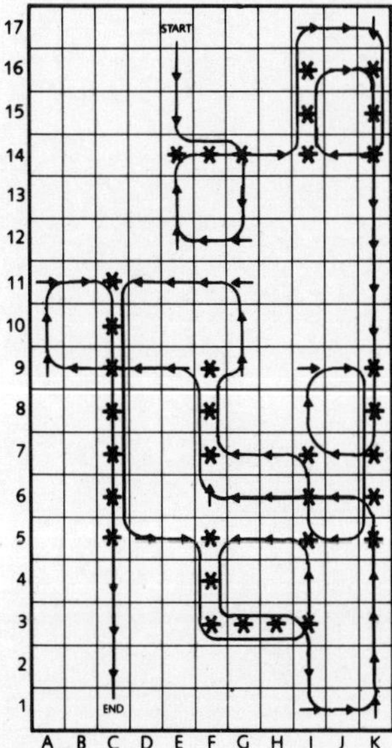

MAZE PHRASE OF PHILOS

In this chart F means forward towards the centre of the spiral and B backwards towards Start.

F3	F5	B3	B3	F5	B3	F5	F3	F3	F3	B5
R	E	D	✱	S	K	Y	✱	A	T	✱

F3	B5	F3	F3	F3	F3	F5	B3	B3	B3	F5
N	I	G	H	T	✱	Y	O	U	R	✱

F3	F3	F5	F3	B5	F3	B5	B5	F3	F3	F5	B3	F5	F3	
R	O	O	F	✱	I	S	✱	A	L	I	G	H	T	END

SUM MAZE

Here is a way to score 49 points. Any advance?

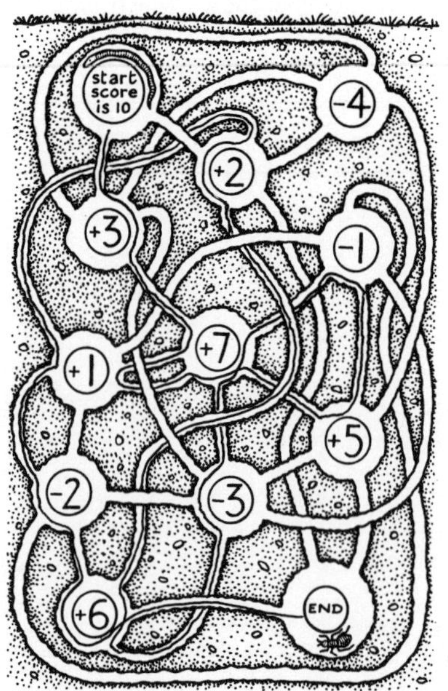

INITIATIVE TESTS

TIME FOR THE BUS

The 6.18 is bus number 3. The number of each bus is the hour it departs divided into the minutes: thus 3 into 24 goes 8.

FRUIT SALAD

Grape; apple; lemon; peach. The letters of each word are set out in alternate squares.

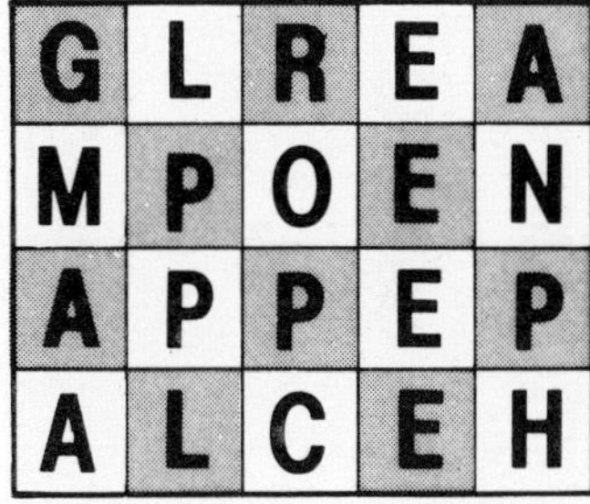

SWITCH WORD

Heights is in the wrong group and should join the other. Outworn, listening, money and canine all have numbers spelled out within them, as does h*eight*s.

DON'T TOUCH

S. Going round the square in a spiral from the top right hand corner spells DANGEROUS.

GET THE PICTURE

D. The King of Spades. In each line across and down the faces look alternatively left and right. Of the four remaining court cards only the King of Spades looks right.

LINKS

C: Flower. In each line across the middle picture has a link with the two either side:
WALL PAPER WEIGHT
(wallpaper and paperweight)
NOSE BAG PIPE
(nosebag and bagpipe)
Flower completes sunflower and flowerbed.

PICK A PIC

B: the belt. the pictures show
Match, ?, Pin
Bolt Cup
Each word has just one vowel; A, I, O, U. Only Belt had E to complete the set of vowels.

CUP TIED

Bert did not win the treble chance as the result was DERBY 1 PLYMOUTH 2. The score by each team is simply the number of vowels in that team's printed name.

MEET THE DEALER

Seattle Square: five of clubs. Each row contains one of each suit and the numbers increase by two each time.

Denver Diamond: two of spades. Each line of 3 cards totals 15. Cards above the value of a five are all diamonds and the rest are spades.

Toledo Triangle: King of clubs. The number value of each card is found by adding together the values of the two cards above it. The suits hearts, clubs, diamonds, spades, spiral from left to right.

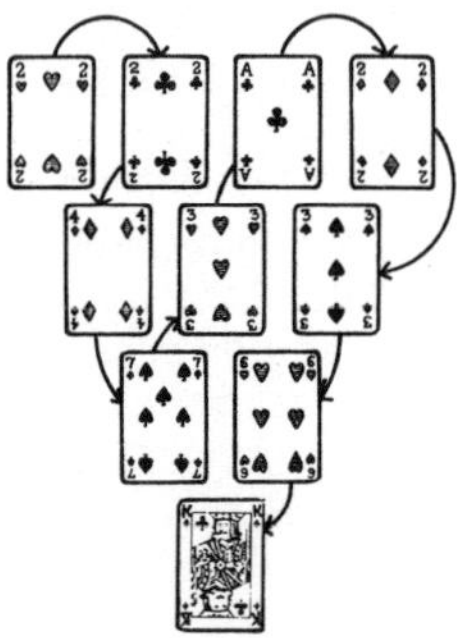

NUMBER PLEASE

The missing number is 3. Either you can see the series 1; 1, 2; 1, 2, 3; 1, 2, 3, 4; 1, 2, 3, 4, 5 going clockwise around the rectangle or you could say that there are five 1's, four 2's, two 4's and one 5. So a 3 is needed to make three 3's.

JEKYLL & HYDE

Reading diagonally left to right the letters spell MORECAMBE AND WISE.

MISSING LINK

C: the bun. In each line across the three words rhyme:

Tune	Gun	Car
Moon	Sun	Star
Balloon.	Bun.	Jar.

MISSING FOUR

The letters have been sown in every other square starting from the top left corner and returning to the adjacent square when the bottom right corner is reached.

A	I	B	J
K	C	L	D
E	M	F	N
O	G	P	H

NINEWORDS

1. Marmalade.
2. Telescope.
3. Badminton.
4. Delicious.
5. Exploring.
6. Noiseless.
7. Overspend.
8. Yesterday.
9. Acrobatic.

POETIC JUSTICE

Lady Silvia da Quincy did the foul deed. The first and last letters of each line form her name.

IN THE PICTURE

B: the book. The middle picture in each line acts as a link between the two end pictures.
Handcuff – cufflink.
Applecart – cartwheel.
Logbook – bookworm.

WHODUNNIT?

SPEAR MURDER

Bert Crabtree, the plumber, was in the library and did the dirty deed. For the record, the others were disposed as follows: Conservatory – Hon Histodd. Dining room – Miss Spinks. TV Room – Tara Lotte. Morning Room – Lavinia Scrownge. Music Room – Sir Arthur Legoffe. Billiards Room – Gravell. Cloakroom – Elspeth. Lounge – Lady Tayble.

PIC FIT THREE E

PIC FIT TWO D

PIC FIT ONE B

PIC FIT FOUR C

VICTORY ON PAPER

Harry Scott is holding the cup. In all the pictures he is the only left-hander.

THE LONG SHOT

No, Alphonse did not get away with it and was convicted of murder.

The witness only heard one shot yet two were fired. If the shots sounded simultaneous to him then the man who was a long way away must have fired first for the sound of his shot to reach the witness's ears at the same time as the sound from the nearby gun.

VISITING TIME

Marie Suggett, the director's wife, is the guilty party.

The four couples are: Sonia and Cedric Davies, surgeon. Clare and James Finch, broker. Alison and Andrew Marsh, painter. Marie and Peter Suggett, director.

The schedule was:

8.40 Mr Davies, Mr Finch and Mrs Davies went in.

8.50 Mrs Davies left. Mr Suggett, Mr Marsh, Mrs Finch went in.

9.05 Messrs Davies, Marsh, Suggett left, then Mrs Suggett went in.

9.30 Mr and Mrs Finch left – leaving Mrs Suggett alone in the room with the patient before Mrs Marsh went in.

9.50 Mrs Marsh and Mrs Suggett left.

OPEN AND SHUT CASE

The man with the hat should be arrested. His case is identical to the one in the picture, the others differ in some detail of the zips around the case and pocket.

CROMWELL'S REVENGE

The sentry on duty had committed the terrible crime of being asleep cat his post! How else could he have 'just had a dream'?

TRUTH WILL OUT

If you have popped in for a bit of help, let us just rid ourselves of the rest by saying straight away: Alf drove the van, Bert bunged the brick and Charlie waved the gun around. Alf told the truth, Bert told one lie and Charlie told two lies.

Right. Have the clever clogs gone? Good, gather round.

The secret is simply to assume that one of the three told the truth – so pick anybody you like and treat their remarks as if they are correct. Who would you like? Bert? He'll do.

If Bert told the truth then Alf drove the van, Charlie threw the brick and so Bert must have waved the gun around.

Check these 'facts' against Alf's statements.

He says he drove the van – which would be true – and Bert threw the brick – which would be false. OK so far.

Now check Charlie's statements.

Bert waved the gun around – which would be true – and Charlie drove the van – which would be false.

So if Bert is telling the truth then the other two have told one lie each, which we are informed did not happen.

So Bert is not the truth teller.

If you take Charlie's statements to be true you will find that both Alf and Bert told two lies – so Charlie is not the truth teller either.

Therefore Alf must have told the truth – which means Alf drove, Bert bunged and Charlie waved.

All clear? Jolly good. Off you go then.

LORRY LOAD OF LIES

Barry was the guest of honour at the local magistrates court.

DOUBLE TROUBLE

Slugger tried to break the lock. Toddy sprayed the gas. Ugly rammed the van.

CAUGHT NAPPING

Mugsy set the ladder up. Patsy wrote the note. Sudsy climbed in the window.

SWEET REASON

Marcus took the sweets and Marcus also ran away with them. No matter which of the two boys lies completely both lead to Marcus taking the bag. So that makes Sheila's first statement true. Therefore she lied when she said that Johnny ran off with it. So Marcus must have done, naughty lad.

SHOPPING AROUND

Jenny created the diversion while Karen passed the goods to Helen who took them out of the shop.

DON'T BANK ON IT

Joe guarded the staff. Klive grabbed the cash. Limey cut the alarm.

FRAUDULENT CONVERSION

Fergus collected the money from the bank. Gerald changed the computer program. Howard copied the key.

PEACH SURPRISE

Sid Woodward was murdered by Charles Dent.

Reading clockwise around the table, the dinner party was:

Eric Carter: steak and ice cream.

Phil England: pork chop and cheese.
Bert Hunter: game pie and fresh fruit.
Sid Woodward: duck and quite a peach surprise.
Charles Dent: trout and trifle.

TEAM GAMES

FUR ENOUGH

The lady had weighed herself and been dissatisfied with the machine's verdict. She was about to try again when she suddenly had what she thought was a brainwave. She took off her heavy fur coat and carefully placed it over her arm before stepping back on the scales! She was very disappointed to see it made no difference to her weight.

RIDDLE OF THE CRYING MAN

One man is a prisoner, the other a prison officer. The convict had taken the advantage of a roadside stop to pull a gun on the guard and demand that the handcuffs binding them together be opened. The officer decided to make a fight of it and put the key in his mouth to free his one usable hand and tackle the gunman. In panic the prisoner shot him and the officer *swallowed the key*. So the criminal cannot get away from the man he has just killed.

UNLUCKY THIRTEEN

Take a deep breath for this one . . . The man was simply a very, very *bad conductor*!

FIELD FIND

Vincent made his journey in early spring soon after the snow had melted. The same snow which the village children had used to make a snowman which they decorated with coal for eyes, nose and coat buttons and carrot for a mouth.

DASH IT

The lady in the house was an actress rehearsing an Agatha Christie thriller. She was practising her dying screams for the end of act one and the passing man had thought it real and rushed in to save her.

FIRST – AND LAST – ORDER

The man had hiccups. He asked for a glass of water to cure them but the barman knew that a sudden shock is also a good cure. So he pulled the gun. The method worked and the man thanked him for his medicinal help.

LATE LAMENTED

Fred and Freda are, or rather were, goldfish. It was the cat who had pulled the cloth on which their bowl was standing, sending it crashing to the floor and causing the startled feline to make a quick exit.

THE HOUSE CALL

Henry Kingsbury, shame on him, was a burglar. He had entered the unlit house by a back window and made his way to the lounge. The glowing fire reminded him how cold he was so he thought he would warm up before doing his dastardly deeds.

He was shocked when a voice behind him said 'Stick 'em up!' and, being non-violent, he did. What caused his collapse was when the voice continued by saying 'Have a nut,' and 'Who's a pretty boy, then?' and he realized he had been arrested by the owner's parrot.

DOMESTIC TIFF

Mrs Platt did outwork for a computer firm and had to thread 3,000 components onto the wire. After a tiring evening threading and counting she was near the end of her labours when the telehone rang. Her husband answered it and said 'Hello. Sicklehampton 2496.' She lost count.

KNEES DOWN

Two five-a-side football teams plus one referee are searching for a contact lens lost by one of the players.

AH – AGH!

As I heard it, this was a true story which happened a long time ago. The two men were playing chess and one suddenly saw a move which would give him checkmate. He stood up in triumph but forgot that, absorbed in the game, he had wrapped a leg around the leg of the table. Standing up like that severely damaged his leg. (No mention is made of what happened to the table.)

All of which proves that even chess can be a dangerous game.

THE DEATH CALL

The man was a fisherman and had just made the catch of a lifetime. He had phoned his wife to tell her about it and she had, naturally, asked how big the fish was. He answered, like every angler before him, with his arms. His last words as his hands went through the glass which slashed his wrists were: 'It was THAT big!'

DOWN – AND OUT

The man has found a very rare parking space so he has sent his wife to fetch the family car.

STRINGING YOU ALONG

The couple were on a long ride late at night and their windscreen wiper motor had broken. The lady had tied a string to each wiper blade and for many miles she had tugged back and forth to keep the blades going.

I could not supply or fit another motor so they just had to keep going.

SHORT STOP

We were looking for the way to open the bonnet. The man had borrowed the car from a friend who told him it needed oil. He didn't like to call in and just ask for help since he could not find the bonnet catch himself so he bought the petrol first and then asked.

I don't recall what make of car it was, it had a wooden fascia, but though we searched all over neither of us could find a way to get the bonnet open.

A FERRY CLOSE AFFAIR

The officer told our young leaper that the ferry was coming in, not leaving as he had supposed.

A MOVING EXPERIENCE

He is standing on an underground escalator trying to pencil in a beard and moustache on an advertisement's face. As the escalator descends he must lean forward and eventually run back up a few steps in order to stay where he is. When he has finished he stands still and the machinery takes him down.

BUS STOP

The bus was on a through route from Wolverhampton to Worcester. The man had joined the bus at Wolverhampton and asked for a ticket to Birmingham. Unfortunately he fell asleep before reaching that city.

He was still asleep when the conductor came to ask for the fares. On being woken up he did not believe that he had slept right through Birmingham and insisted that he had already paid his fare.

Eventually he saw the light and the conductor kindly stopped the bus opposite a stop where the man could catch a bus back to Birmingham.

LITTLE BOY BLUE

The lad told the policeman that he had run away from home but was not yet old enough to cross the road.

CARDBOARD & COUNTERS

COIN OP

(Or its mirror image, switched left to right.)

20p	5p	1p
2p	50p	10p

CHANGE IN THE WEATHER

One way to do it in 22 moves:
2 to 7. 1 to 6. 7 to 1. 9 to 2. 8 to 4. 6 to 8. 4 to 6. 2 to 9. 1 to 7. 6 to 1. 3 to 6. 7 to 3. 9 to 2. 10 to 4. 6 to 10. 4 to 6. 2 to 9. 3 to 7. 6 to 3. 7 to 6. 9 to 2. 6 to 9.

SQUARE AROUND

The main problem can be solved in 21 moves if, at a particular stage, you move L in at one door and on the next move take L out again by the same door! Start by moving A out of the bottom door. Then move the following letters into the adjacent space: L, I, N, U, O and A in at the top door. L out at the bottom door. I, N, A moved into space left and L in at top door. L out at top door. O, U, I, N, A, I, N moved and L in at bottom door.

OVER KNIGHT STOP

Just 8 moves are needed:
A to E to F. I to E to A. C to D to I. H to G to D to C. B to G to H. F to E. J to F to B. E to F to J.

QUEENS HIGH

Fatima is yours if you scored 63 points by placing the queens at the circled numbers. Her sister requires a score of 67.

FATIMA

6 2 4 1 ⑨ 3 6 5
7 3 2 0 3 1 ⑧ 0
⑨ 1 6 9 0 5 1 6
0 5 ⑨ 8 0 8 2 4
0 9 1 2 6 5 5 ⑨
6 9 7 0 2 ⑨ 0 2
1 8 0 ① 7 2 8 2
9 ⑨ 1 2 4 3 8 4

MINIMA

1 2 7 2 8 ⑧ 8 1
4 3 ⑨ 9 6 4 4 4
1 3 5 6 3 7 ⑧ 6
4 ⑨ 0 5 2 7 9 7
6 1 6 5 1 8 7 ⑨
4 3 5 1 ⑨ 7 8 5
⑦ 2 1 1 7 2 3 5
6 7 9 ⑧ 2 1 8 9

HIGH DIE HI!

Fifty points can be scored in the 3 by 3 square as follows:
right, down, right, down, left, up, left, down, right, right, up, up, left, down, left, up.

6	6	6
6	4	5
6	6	5

Sixty points can be scored in the second problem by moving:
down, right, up, left, right, down, right, down, down, right, up, left, left, down, right, up, right, down, left, up, left, up, right, down, down, right, up, left, left, left, up.

5	5		
6	6	6	
6	4	1	5
	5	5	6

Can It Be Beaten?

To give you something to shoot at, here is a target of 69 points for the third picture:
down, right, up, left, right, down, right, down, right, up, left, down, left, left, up, down, right, up, down, right, right, right, up, left, down, left, up, right, right, up.

5	5			6
6	6	6	2	6
6	6	5	4	6

CALCULATOR'S CORNER

SPOT THE NUMBER

Thirty points are yours if you have these or an equally good alternative.

A. 3 × 6 + 14.
B. 23 − (5 − 2)
C. (4 − 1) − (6 − 4)
D. 56 − 23
E. 25 − (3 × 4)
F. 32 + (3 − 3)
G. (5 + 6) × 55
H. 554 ÷ 2
I. (3 + 2) × 6 − 1
J. 666 ÷ 6

DIGITAL SPLITS

There is more than one way to de-fur this particular domestic pet so we give the top score (we hope!) and one way of achieving it.

A. 8173. 532 + 7641.
B. 9377. 632 + 8745.
C. 13942. 7510 + 6432.
D. 2538 861 + 932 + 745.
E. 18197. 8432 + 9765.

CASH, BANG, WALLET

Cascade: 1p, 2p, 10p, 10p, 20p.
Cost: 43p
Etna: 5p, 5p, 10p, 10p, 20p.
Cost: 50p
Rocket: 1p, 2p, 2p, 2p, 50p.
Cost: 57p

MAGIC SWITCH

Switching four pairs of numbers which are symmetrically opposite through the centre will do the trick.

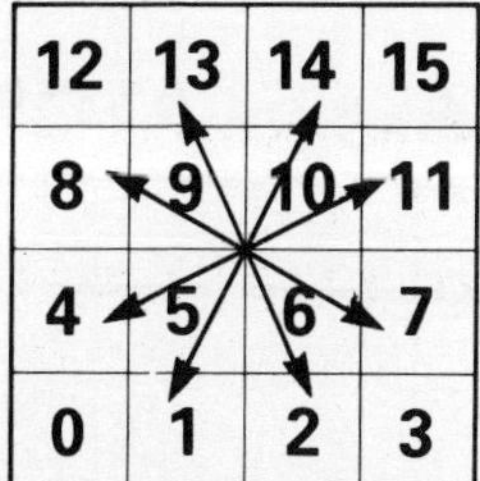

12	2	1	15
7	9	10	4
11	5	6	8
0	14	13	3

SUM TROUBLE

		6		5			
	3	+	6	−	2	=	7
2	×	4	−	5	=	3	
	5	×	1	×	5	=	25
9	+	2	+	4	=	15	
	1	=	7	=			
	=	20	=	0			
	16		12				

SHARE ROBBERY

There were 56 bars in the original haul.

Jimmy found one, which added to the one hidden under the floor by Ferdie gives two, which is a quarter of the pile that crook found. So Ferdie found eight bars; add the one hidden by Clogger gives nine, which is one third of the heap which Clogger put his hands on. This gives 27 bars and again adding the 1 under the floorboard deposited by Alf gives 28, which is half the original pile.

SUM SCORE

A. 44 − (4 − 4) scores 5 points.
B. (5 × 5) + (5 × 5) + 5 scores 3 points.
C. 66 − 66 + 66 scores 5 points.
D. (7 × 7) + (7 × 7) − 7 − 7 − 7 scores 3 points.
E. 888 − 888 + 88 scores 5 points.

TOP DISPLAY

9 ÷ 1 + 7 − 2 × 6 = 84

FARE PLEASE

Twenty-two 2p coins were in the bag.

The total fare in pence, 979, is 89 × 11. Since there never are many passengers it cannot mean 89 people paying 11p each so it must be 11 passengers paying 89p. However that amount is made up using seven coins, it must contain just two 2p coins.

SUM TOTAL

	4	3	9	= 16
	8	5	1	= 14
	2	6	7	= 15
16 (diagonal)	= 14	= 14	= 17	16 (diagonal)

JOLLY GOOD SHOW

MULTIPLICATION (2)

×	8	3	2	4	9	1	7	6	5
7	56	21	14	28	63	7	49	42	35
2	16	6	4	8	18	2	14	12	10
4	32	12	8	16	36	4	28	24	20
5	40	15	10	20	45	5	35	30	25
8	64	24	16	32	72	8	56	48	40
1	8	3	2	4	9	1	7	6	5
3	24	9	6	12	27	3	21	18	15
6	48	18	12	24	54	6	42	36	30
9	72	27	18	36	81	9	63	54	45

ADDITION (1)

+	8	5	0	9	2
7	15	12	7	16	9
4	12	9	4	13	6
1	9	6	1	10	3
6	14	11	6	15	8
3	11	8	3	12	5

MULTIPLICATION (1)

×	5	6	2	8	3
7	35	42	14	56	21
0	0	0	0	0	0
9	45	54	18	72	27
1	5	6	2	8	3
4	20	24	8	32	12

ADDITION (2)

+	3	1	7	9	2
4	7	5	11	13	6
0	3	1	7	9	2
8	11	9	15	17	10
6	9	7	13	15	8
5	8	6	12	14	7